WATTSON BROTHERS GO WEST

BG Hines

Fulton Books
Meadville, PA

Published by Fulton Books 2022

ISBN 979-8-88505-788-2 (paperback)
ISBN 979-8-88505-789-9 (digital)

Printed in the United States of America

PROLOGUE

TWO MEN SLOWLY followed a dusty, hollowed-out mountain path leading down a narrow valley to the Aegean Sea. A tall broad-shouldered man with coarse white hair leaned heavily on a shorter, younger man. His muscular left arm was thrown over his companion's neck while his right arm stretched across his stomach. His large hand tightly gripped his left side.

"Not too much farther, Mr. Wattson, only a mile or so," said the younger man, Dailey.

"I don't know, pal, a mile or so seems like a mighty long way right now," said his friend with a smile that turned into a grimace. A little later, he sagged against the younger man and almost fell.

"Are you hurting badly?"

"I'm okay, but let's stop for a minute." He turned and, with his friend's help, slowly sat down on a flat rock and leaned against a small tree trunk.

Standing back and looking at his injured friend, Dailey noticed blood, drops of blood.

"You're bleeding again, Mr. Wattson."

"Don't think I ever stopped, Dailey. Walk back a little way and see if they're on our trail yet."

"Yes, sir." And he carefully made his way back up the path. Coming to a large boulder by the trail, he climbed it quickly, hoping that he would blend into the trees and not be easily seen from a distance. He stood, shielded his eyes from the bright Grecian sun, and looked back over their route.

At first, he saw nothing, but then through the trees several hundred feet higher, he saw a glint of metal. Carefully looking at this spot, he saw more sunlight flashes and knew they were being followed. Lowering himself from his perch, he started back down the path. He stopped suddenly and, bending over, reached down into the dirt. Straightening up, he rubbed his fingers together and realized the dark spots on the path were blood. That was how they were being tracked.

Hurrying back to his friend, he reached down to help him up.

"Dailey, I think you need to go along without me. I don't think I can make it." He moved his hand from over his rib cage, and it was covered with blood.

"No, sir. I'll carry you if I have to. We're probably a half mile ahead of those people and have less than a mile to go."

"Okay, let's give it a try. I don't think I'll get treated too well if they catch up to us."

"No, sir. The way you threw those soldiers around made a big impression on them."

"Maybe, but I was foolish letting that one guy sneak up on me and stick his spear in my side. I must be getting old to make a mistake like that."

"That wasn't a mistake, you were outnumbered five to one. I just wish I'd shouted a warning sooner."

"Dailey, you were outnumbered too. I think you had your hands full trying to keep them off you."

"Mr. Wattson, I don't think they've ever seen anyone your size."

"Probably not too many men were over six feet during this time. Most were only a little over five feet. I'm getting light-headed, Dailey. We better get going."

"Yes, sir."

With that, Dailey carefully placed his arm around Wattson's waist and steered him down the path. Twenty minutes later, they went between two trees, turned a corner, and they were there. A large, dull, metal saucer-shaped craft sat in the middle of a small clearing in front of them. A ladder extended down the side facing them and led to an opening in the railing circling the top deck. A large sheet of fishnet-like, green material was draped over the saucer's top and down its sides.

"Okay, Dailey, up quick. Open the hatch and pull the net in after you."

"Can you make it, Mr. Wattson?"

"I think so. Hurry now."

Dailey scampered up the ladder and disappeared inside, pulling the camouflage netting after him. Wattson laboriously pulled himself up the rungs. When he reached the top, he leaned back and tried to catch his breath.

Suddenly, he heard yells as five helmeted men rounded the corner and charged toward him. The leading man, ten yards ahead of the others, leaped upward and thrust with an eight-foot spear topped with a leaf-shaped, iron-tipped head. In a flash, Wattson snatched it from his hand and used it to deliver a resounding crack against the bronze helmet, causing his attacker to crumple to the ground. The other four soldiers tripped over one another as they rushed to stop and stay out of range.

Wattson felt hands under his arms as he was quickly helped back to the hatch where he dropped the spear through the opening. He disappeared below, still with Dailey's help who then quickly followed and pulled the hatch cover after him, reaching up and spinning a small handle to lock it shut.

The two men slumped in padded chairs that were riveted to the floor. Their breath came in ragged bursts, but they were finally safe.

Wattson gave a low, soft moan, moved his blood-covered hand to the arm of the chair, and turned to his friend.

"Two things, Dailey, I want you to do for me. One, I want you to take care of my boys and watch over them. Two, will you call me Bill just one time? I never could get you to call me Bill."

A tear rolled down Dailey's cheek as he answered, "Don't worry, sir. I'll look out for the boys. I'm sorry I could never call you Bill, Bill. I've just always respected you so much I couldn't bring myself to do it."

CHAPTER 1

SCHOOL

TIME—A MEASURE OF duration, not a barrier or obstruction.

Bob Wattson stretched out his long legs and laid back on the brown-and-black tweed sofa wedged into a corner of the dorm room he shared with his brother, William. He switched on a brass floor lamp, and it cast a yellow circle in an otherwise dark room. There were twin pine beds with carved acorns topping each of their four posts, a small closet jammed with clothes, and a large dresser with a cracked mirror. Two paintings of sailing ships in chipped, gilded frames, both of which hung crooked, adorned the walls. The only photo in the room, in a silver frame sitting on the dresser, showed a large, smiling man in jeans and a plaid shirt, his arms thrown over two boys' shoulders. The two boys, dressed in shorts, had knobby, adolescent knees and appeared to be about ten years old. Sighing, Bob reached toward an adjoining table for his algebra book, flipped it open, and laid back. Final exams at their New Hampshire private school would start the following week, and he wanted to do well.

The door opened with a bang, and his brother strode into the dorm room. William Wattson tossed some books onto a beat-up, brown leather chair and flopped on the sofa at his brother's feet.

"Been studying?" asked Bob.

"No, not really. I think I have it all down. How about you?

"I'm getting there. However, I don't have your photographic memory."

"Bob, it's been proven there is no such thing as a photographic memory. You're smart, just read the material."

"That's what I'm doing, alphabetical letters to find unknown numbers."

William smiled at his brother's dismay, reached over, and ruffled his hair. "Algebraic expressions, brother."

Bob stood up, laughed, and shook his head of shaggy, brown hair. An imposing figure standing six feet, three inches tall and weighing two hundred and ninety-five pounds, he was heavily muscled and had broad shoulders, big head, hands and feet, and a deep but cheerful voice. He had a slightly upturned nose and wide, hazel eyes hovering above a square, stubble-shrouded jaw.

Bob shoved his hands deep into the pockets of his well-worn khakis. "Do you think it's time to talk with Ellie and Paul?"

"Yeah, I think so. School will end in a few weeks, and we need to know if they want to go with us this summer. It's if they want to and can they do so. We've got to find out one way or the other. Do you think it will be a problem for them to get away?"

"No. I guess being orphans has some advantages. They said all they need to do is tell their guardians they'll be spending the summer working with us on a dude ranch in Wyoming to earn money for school next year. That will take care of it."

"Good. Whose idea was the dude ranch in Wyoming? That's a good touch."

Bob patted himself on the head. "Mine. As far as Ellie and Paul know, they *will* be working on a dude ranch this summer."

William put his hands behind his head and leaned back. "Any question in your mind we can trust them with our secrets?"

"None."

William raised his knees then hopped to his feet. "Good! Then that's settled. Let's get something to eat."

William was known for being decisive and was the older of the two by eleven months. Unlike Bob, he was a slender, six feet, one inch, and weighed one hundred seventy-five pounds, with short, sandy-blond hair neatly parted on the left side. His eyebrows were almost white above startling blue eyes; he had a rather long, straight nose, and unlike his brother, he was clean-shaven. Seldom were two brothers more different in appearance. William looked like their mother while Bob resembled their father.

They didn't remember their mother and had been told she died young and in childbirth, but their father would never talk about her. William once tried to ask his father about her, but when his father's chin dropped to his chest and his face faded into abject sadness, he resolved to never bring it up again.

Because of the closeness of their ages, their father had thought it a good idea to have his sons raised together in the same school class, meaning he had to choose having one a little older for his class or one a little younger. Where their birthdays fell in relation to the school year helped him decide that it was better to have William a little older than his classmates. It seemed to have worked out fine. Both did well in school academically, athletically, and socially. William played basketball and was shortstop and captain of the baseball team. Bob played football and was undefeated as a superheavyweight on the school's wrestling team.

As they left the room, William held the door open for Bob then shut it with a gentle, backward kick. They turned right, walked down polished wood floors to the end of the hall and then down the stairs to the ground floor. They went out the front door, down brick steps, and then followed a concrete path across a grassy lawn. They crossed a quad formed by four wooden, two-story buildings, went up steps, and walked into the school cafeteria. The room had a high ceiling with huge beams spanning its width, shiny wood floors, and heavy wood tables with scarred, varnished tops, and had rustic ladder back chairs with dark-green corduroy cushions. Stacks of glasses, white china plates, cutlery bins, and dun-colored plastic trays were arranged along the back wall. A cafeteria line ran thirty feet: first salads, then desserts, followed by meats, and finally vegetables and bread. It ended at a wall comprised of large windows facing a lake that could be glimpsed through trees. Hungry students began filling the room quickly.

As they pushed their trays down the metal serving line, Bob received friendly greetings from several cooks. He was known for his appetite as well as for his appreciative attitude toward the kitchen staff. He responded to these greetings with joking banter that in each case was received with a smile and retort.

A large lady in a white apron, with blond hair held in a tight net, stood on the serving side of the cafeteria line. Seeing Bob approach, she poised her serving tongs over a huge tray of fried chicken. "Why, look who's here? Bob, I knew you didn't care for fried chicken, so I had the kitchen staff make you some broiled liver. If you'll wait just a minute, I'll go get it for you."

"Miss Betsy, I don't want to put you to that trouble. Just for you and just this time, I'll try to get by with fried chicken. Tell you what, to show you I'm appreciative, go on and put three pieces on my plate. I'll do my best to eat a little bit of it."

"Why, Bob, that is so nice of you. I may give you four pieces." And she winked at Bob and did exactly that.

After filling their trays, they looked for a vacant table. Almost immediately, two students sitting next to a large double window called them over. William and Bob moved to the table, set down their trays, and pulled up chairs to join Paul and Ellie, their two closest friends at school and in the world.

They had all been close since meeting as wide-eyed seventh graders during orientation. None of the four had been accompanied by parents, and they had just gravitated toward one another. Now they were as close as siblings: three brothers and a little sister.

Eleanor Heath, "Ellie" to her friends, was petite with flaming-red hair and a pretty, perky face. She hated her freckles, but all the boys admired them. From Sandy Springs, Georgia, she was William's age and had a happy, sunny disposition. She was a cheerleader and a gymnast. Her parents had died in an automobile accident when she was four, and she had been raised by an assortment of relatives. She attended school on an academic scholarship. She was dressed in navy shorts with a multicolored Mexican belt, a white polo shirt, and neon-green Nike running shoes. Paul Lioni sat next to her. Tall, with wide shoulders, dark hair, and liquid, black eyes, Paul wore his usual uniform of faded jeans, a green Dartmouth T-shirt, and scuffed deck shoes. He was from Ithaca, New York. His father had died in the

World Trade Center on 9/11, and his mother died only a few months later after a brief illness. Bob described his friend as a good Italian Yankee. Paul said he was only half Italian, but as he liked to say, it was "the good half." He played football with Bob, basketball and baseball with William, and was class vice president. He also had no shortage of female admirers at school.

They finished their meals and leaned their chairs back onto two legs. Bob was getting one extra helping of cherry pie when William suggested that Paul and Ellie come by their room later. There was something he and Bob wanted to discuss with them.

"Discuss what?" asked Ellie.

With a hint of mystery, William said they would have to wait to find out.

The Wattson brothers walked back to their room and settled into their usual spots: William on the sofa working a crossword puzzle and Bob propped against his headboard with his algebra book.

A few minutes later, there was a knock at the door, and they asked Ellie and Paul to come in. Ellie sat on the sofa next to William, and Paul took the large leather chair. Bob spun on the bed, draped his legs over the side, and sat up.

"Okay, what are we discussing?" intoned Ellie.

William turned in her direction, "Well, we won't be at a dude ranch this summer."

"Then where will we be?"

"Dad had a special home in Wyoming. Bob and I sometimes use it. We'll be staying there, part of the time."

"And the rest of the time?"

William looked at his brother. "Bob, the rest of the time?"

"We'll be out in the Montana and Wyoming wilderness most of the time. I think everyone will enjoy it."

"Doing what?" asked Ellie.

"Riding around looking at the country and probably getting in some hiking and camping. We thought you would like it since you've never been out west."

"Well, okay, I'm game. Paul, how about you?'

"I was looking forward to making a little money this summer, but I still will have some coming in from Social Security. I'm not familiar with having money anyway, so it should be fine."

Ellie looked at William. "What do we need to take?"

"Underwear, socks, and traveling clothes. Anything else you can think of, William?" Bob responded.

"Nope, that will about do it. We have all the equipment we'll need."

"Nothing else?" asked Ellie.

"A toothbrush," joked Bob.

CHAPTER 2

WYOMING

THE NEXT TWO weeks flew by with studying, exams, and saying goodbyes to classmates for the summer. The four friends all did well on their examinations, with William leading the way. This was to the surprise of no one. Ellie and Paul worked out their summer schedules with their guardians, and soon everyone was packed and ready to go. They loaded their bags into William's ten-year-old Jeep Wrangler. Ellie and Paul sat in back, and Bob squeezed into the passenger seat next to William. In three hours, the four had driven through the White Mountains, checked their bags, and passed through airport security.

As they boarded their plane at the Manchester airport, the friends had no idea of the adventure that lay ahead. William and Ellie sat together and immediately started talking about their school year. Bob and Paul luckily had an empty seat between them since the two of them, mostly Bob, took up three seats. As the plane took off, Paul looked out the window. A khaki cap with a red-embroidered "JH" was over Bob's eyes, and he was fast asleep.

William turned to Ellie and asked, "How did your parents' accident happen?"

"I was really too young to remember much. They were in Atlanta Christmas shopping, and it happened on the freeway. That's really all I know. I was staying with my father's sister that weekend, and she came in and told me. I really didn't understand, but she was crying, so I started crying. Doesn't tell you much, huh?" she said somberly.

"What happened then?"

"Well, my aunt was single, worked, and wasn't able to keep me. That kind of started my moving from family to family. I wasn't bad, I made good grades and was never a problem, but things just never worked out so that anyone could keep me permanently. Sometimes it was money, sometimes too many children were already there, whatever. When I found out about our school and that it had a scholarship program for poor but deserving kids, I qualified and applied. Luckily, they accepted me, and here I am."

"You don't have brothers or sisters?"

"Nope, you and Bob are like the brothers I never had. At least, I love you both like brothers. You two and the school seem to be the family and home I never really had. This will probably sound awful to say, but I hate going home for the summer. That's why I was so excited to be spending this summer in Wyoming with you two and Paul."

Several hours later, the friends sat at a gate in the Denver airport and waited for their next flight to board. Ellie leaned over to Paul and said, "Okay, I told William a little about my upbringing. Now you tell us about yours. You've never really talked about your family."

Paul reached over and patted her on the head. "I thought where you come from, they call it 'raising.'"

"Okay, tell us about your raising," said Ellie as she swatted at his hand.

"Probably like most people, I guess. After my parents both died, I moved in with my grandparents…Dad's parents. I tried never to be a problem and think I did a pretty good job of it. Mine is a big Italian family with lots of cousins, aunts, and uncles. There were always lots of people around. It was pretty nice."

"How did you end up at our school?" asked Bob.

"A friend of my father's had gone to school there. One day, he called and asked to speak to me and my grandparents. He came over the next day and told us what a good friend my father had been to him when he was going through a hard time with his business. Then got a little emotional, told us about the school and what a good education you could get there, and offered to pay my tuition. I asked for a little time to talk it over with my grandparents. He was okay with that. Later that week, I called him and accepted the offer. That's how I got to your fancy school and met you, guys."

Seven hours, a change of planes, and twenty-three hundred miles later, William Wattson looked out of the window at the snow-capped, spiked peaks of the Teton Mountain Range. They were silhouetted against the clear blue skies above Jackson, Wyoming. He was happy to be almost home. As they turned south to begin the descent into the airport, William could see the well-named Snake River as it twisted and turned across the valley floor that gave the area its name.

The big jet landed with a screech and puff of smoke from the tires as they met the runway. The pilot reversed the engines, applied brakes, and soon they were taxiing to a small, rustic airport terminal. It sat on the valley floor, practically at the base of Grand Teton, the second tallest mountain in the state.

The pilot's voice came over the intercom, "Welcome to Jackson Hole, Wyoming. Jackson Hole is the valley, Jackson is the town. The temperature is fifty-two degrees, with the wind out of the north at five miles an hour. As the sign says at the city limits, *the last of the old west.*"

William turned to Ellie with a smile. "Just another summery day in northwest Wyoming."

Bob and Paul waited at the foot of the stairs leading down from the plane's door. "When is summer in Jackson Hole?" Paul asked with a laugh as a light breeze bathed them in the chilled but sparkling clean Wyoming air.

With a big, impish grin, Bob replied, "Summer? That was last week."

The friends walked across the tarmac, under an arch of elk horns, and into the terminal. "Around to the right is baggage pickup," instructed William.

As they rounded the corner, William jumped as a voice boomed out, "William, I'm glad to see you and Bob!"

William turned and was crushed in a bear hug by a heavyset man with a long, white beard. He was dressed in jeans, scuffed cowboy boots, a frayed red-plaid cowboy shirt, and a worn, pearl-gray cowboy hat with a narrow, braided leather hatband circling the crown.

"Dailey, I'm glad to see you too!" said William.

Bob came over to Dailey and hugged him, lifting him off his feet. As Bob set Dailey back down, he turned to his friends, "Guys, this is Dailey Jones. He was our dad's best friend."

Dailey Jones had been Bill Wattson's right-hand man for as long as they could remember. He continued to run things for the boys after their father died three years earlier. When they traveled back east to boarding school, he handled their school bills and allowances. Dailey was a beloved uncle, surrogate father, and trusted friend to William and Bob. He had been in their lives since they were born.

A buzzer sounded, and they gathered with the other passengers to collect their bags off the moving conveyor belt. Soon all the bags were accounted for, and they moved toward the parking lot beyond.

Dailey led them to a dusty, silver, four-door four-wheel-drive pickup truck. They tossed their bags onto its bed and loaded up. As Bob was the largest, he sat in the front seat next to Dailey. Being the smallest, Ellie sat between the other two boys on the back seat.

As they turned south on Highway 191 toward Jackson, Bob said, "There's the Sleeping Indian."

"Where? I don't see an Indian," replied Paul.

"Look at the top of that mountainside to your left. What do you see?"

Ellie and Paul's eyes followed Bob's finger, and there, at the top, was the shape of a reclining person, complete with nose and war bonnet.

"Wow! It does look like a reclining Indian!" said Ellie.

Dailey looked over his shoulder. "Are you, guys, hungry?"

"Yes!" they all said.

"I am starving!" added Bob.

"Where do you want to eat?"

Bob scratched his head. "I wish I could say Billy's, but since it's closed, how about Bubba's? I'd love one of their steaks."

"It's right on the way," replied Dailey.

Paul, amused, said, "You're kidding, right? Billy's? Bubba's? What kind of a place is this? We don't have any restaurants named Bubba's where I'm from."

Ellie quickly chimed in, "We do."

William laughed then said, "Well, Billy's was famous for their burgers and waffle fries. Bubba's is famous for their barbeque, but they have steaks and other things as well."

"Dailey, how about Bubba's? I've been thinking about their onion rings," said Bob.

"You're always thinking of food, brother," said William as their friends laughed.

Dailey pulled into the parking lot of a closed hardware store next door to Bubba's, and they all walked inside. People crowded the small entrance area, but fortunately, most were paying and on their way out. The room stretched directly back and widened to the left. There were booths along the wall next to the windows and a lighted salad bar in the center with a wagon wheel, multi-lit chandelier hanging above it. Glossy, wooden tables, chairs, and booths were set off by western art hanging on the walls. Several tables were available, and the group was soon seated. Almost immediately, a smiling server put paper placemats and plastic menus in front of them. Five minutes later, their drink orders arrived, and they placed their food orders.

For the next hour, Bob entertained them all with his descriptions of the steak, new potatoes, and onion rings. All except Ellie had steaks. True to her southern roots, she ordered and enjoyed baby back ribs.

"These are as good as you can get in Georgia," Ellie said as she licked barbeque sauce off her fingertips.

After they finished, Dailey paid the bill, and everyone walked to the truck. Dailey adjusted his rearview mirror, pulled out of the parking lot, and headed south on 191.

After ten minutes, 191 bore east at Hobach Junction, and they followed it. The road wound down the river canyon with cliffs on both sides and crossed the Hobach River nine times over the next few miles.

"They must have spent a fortune on bridges in this state," remarked Paul as Dailey drove them over the last bridge.

South of the little town of Bondurant, Dailey pulled off the road and stopped in front of a barbed-wire gate. Bob hopped out, lifted the wire loop off the gatepost, and walked the gate open. After they drove through the gate, Bob refastened it and climbed back into the front seat. The truck's headlights lit up a dirt road, which they followed for a winding five miles back into the foothills of the Wind River Range. They curved around a high-rock corner and drove into a narrow canyon, which they followed for a mile. Its sides got progressively higher and closer together.

Giving Dailey a light rap on the shoulder, Bob spoke to his friend. "Dailey, it sure is good seeing you again. I have missed you and missed home."

"I've sure missed you and William. Taking care of everything keeps me busy, but I've missed you two stumbling around and getting in my way," he said with a laugh.

Suddenly, illuminated by their headlights, a large metal building appeared, filling up most of the end of the canyon. It looked to be at least a hundred feet long, a typical industrial building with a gabled, raised-rib, metal roof but no windows, doors, or signage. The totally nondescript building divulged nothing of its purpose or of what was inside. Dailey reached up to his visor and pressed a button on a garage-door opener. On the closest end of the building, a double-garage door rolled up, and spotlights came on. They were so bright white in the dark night that it was almost blinding. Dailey drove inside and parked next to a tall stack of wooden crates, and reaching up again, he closed the door behind them. Equipment filled the building: snowmobiles, recreational vehicles, two more pickups like the one Dailey was driving, a Jeep, and some heavy equipment, including a snowplow. It all was clean, shiny, and ready to use.

"Why all of this?" asked Paul.

William answered, "Work and play. Either play like the snowmobiles and four-wheelers, or work like the snowplow. The weather is tough around here because the elevation is nearly seven thousand feet. Every bit of it will get used during winter."

"Dailey, you keep everything spotless," remarked William.

"I keep it the way your father liked it kept, which is also the way I like it kept."

CHAPTER 3

━━━━━◦━━━━━

THE HOME

"Is THIS YOUR father's house?" asked Ellie as she stepped out of the truck, her eyes wandering around the building. "I mean it's nice but kind of cold inside."

William smiled, "No, Ellie. But we're getting there."

William walked over to the corrugated-metal back wall and pushed something the others couldn't see. That part of the wall swung open and revealed another door. It was six feet wide and more like a bank vault door. Two rows of illuminated buttons on the right side had one through six on the top row, and the bottom row had the letters A through F.

William pushed a combination of buttons from both rows, and the door hissed open like a pressure lock. He flipped a switch that slowly lit up fluorescent bulbs and revealed a passageway that seemed to be carved out of stone. The light showed a flat rock floor angling upward, nine-foot rock walls, and a rock ceiling. The row of lights seemed odd suspended down the left side of the ceiling.

"Why are the lights down the side and not in the middle of the ceiling?" asked Paul.

William smiled. "Dad was always thinking. He said when you took something down this passageway, you always went down the middle, which meant that you could hit and break lights if they're hung there."

William led the way as the group got their bags and filed up the tunnel. After fifty feet, they were at another steel door, with another set of letters and numbers set in a metal panel on the wall to the right of the door. Again, William punched in a combination, and the door slid silently into the wall behind the steel frame. Extremely thick, the door had five heavy rods extending from its side into the wall. As they looked through it, they could see even more doors; these led to an elevator. William moved forward and pushed the elevator's OPEN button. After they all entered, Bob pushed the UP button. The elevator rose slowly for thirty seconds, stopped, and the door slid open.

"We must be really high up in the mountain," said Paul. "That was a pretty long ride."

"At the highest level, we'll be several hundred feet above the valley floor," answered William.

After exiting the elevator, the friends walked down a short corridor with a metal grate floor, turned a corner, and saw yet another steel door, just like the last one.

As William punched in the combination, Ellie turned to him, "Why the funny L-shape?"

"I can tell you what I think, Ellie."

"Okay, what do you think?"

"Dad wanted to make it as difficult as possible to get into his home's innermost part. He told me a story about people firing armor-piercing shells into bank-vault doors during some of the turmoil in the Middle East. He didn't want them to be able to do it here."

"All they would have to do is walk around that corner and lay explosives against the door."

"Nope. Look carefully at the metal floor. It automatically withdraws into the wall. If someone tried to walk down this hall without punching in the correct combination or wearing the right gear, they would find a fifty-foot drop to the rocks below us. I don't think anyone can fire around a corner or walk on air."

"Isn't that a little overkill?" inquired Ellie.

"I think so, but Dad didn't," said William as his finger paused over one of the letters.

William finished putting in the code, and they rode a second elevator slowly upward for another forty-five seconds. The door opened, and they walked into a room nearly fifty feet long, ten feet high, and twenty feet wide, with a gray concrete floor and rock walls, flat black ceiling, and several rows of track lighting. Only the middle row was turned on. The heavy Persian rugs scattered about the floor provided a splash of color to the otherwise somber room. Five or six black, overstuffed leather chairs were the only furniture.

"Dad wasn't much of a decorator." Laughed Bob. "He never got around to doing anything with this room. I really don't know what he had in mind for it."

Everyone followed William across the room to a central, concrete staircase that measured fifteen feet across the bottom and narrowed to ten feet at the top. The treads were coated with a honey-colored sealer, and each riser's face sparkled with multihued lights.

"Why the lights on the steps?" asked Paul.

"Dad thought the room too dark and was afraid someone would trip on the stairs. He wanted something eye-catching but didn't want yellow stripes painted on the tread."

Paul bent down to get a closer look. "The clear lights look like crystals or uncut diamonds."

"Good reason for that," replied Bob. "They *are* diamonds."

"Look at the green, red, and yellow," said William. "What if they were really emeralds, rubies, and topaz and not just pretty lights?"

Bob joined in, "Also garnets, sapphires, opals, and who knows what else."

Ellie stood with open mouth and then shook her head. "Where in the world do they all come from? There must be a fortune here."

William reached down to the bottom riser and rubbed a topaz. "They came from all over the world. I'll tell you the when, where, and how a little later."

Paul and Ellie knelt and rubbed gems in amazement.

Ellie leaned back and caught William's shirtsleeve, "I don't know what I expected to see today, but this wasn't it. Is this all for real?"

"Trust me, it's for real. And you haven't seen anything yet," William replied.

They climbed the stairs and walked into yet another remarkable room, this one perhaps a hundred feet long and even deeper than the last one. Every twenty feet down the left side, four large-framed windows were spaced into the wall. High-back, black leather chairs sat in front of each window, and an ornately carved wooden table was next to each chair.

Groupings of comfortable-looking wingback chairs, along with sofas upholstered in gray nubby fabric, adorned the room's right side. Dark wood end tables with curved legs and clawed feet framed the sofas, and each end table boasted a lamp with a Tiffany glass shade in purple, yellow, green, and gold. Navy, cream, and peach Persian rugs added texture and warmth in front of each sofa, and more rugs, these in red, black, and olive, were randomly scattered about the room. They could feel a light air current, and it was a cozy setting for such a big room.

"I guess Dad wanted one room to have some color, and this is that room," said William, looking bemused.

Ellie and Paul sat down in two of the leather chairs that were placed in front of the windows. Paul swiveled around. "These aren't windows. They're television screens."

Ellie spun her chair around as well, perplexed. She asked, "What is this place and who was your father?"

William motioned to a sofa. "Long story. Let's sit over here, and I'll give you the short version."

CHAPTER 4

THE STORY

WILLIAM SAT DOWN on a sofa, and his brother joined him. Paul and Ellie each chose a facing wingback chair. They all settled in, and William began to tell his story:

"Our father was a very wealthy man, the only child of our very wealthy grandfather, who was, oddly enough, the only surviving child of our very, very wealthy great-grandfather. Our family assets were not divided for more than a hundred years so that the family fortune continued growing with each generation.

"Dad was very eccentric in many ways. He never minded taking risks with money. He had lots of it and funded every strange scheme that came his way. Hydrogen power, perpetual motion machines, you name it, and he might have been involved. And though he may have been different, but Dad was also a genius. He held many patents, some of them still lucrative. This should have been the case as over the years he invested millions of dollars. By then, our family fortune was multiplying faster than he could spend or give to charities, and it still is.

"As Dad worked in his office one day, his secretary, Mrs. Price, announced that a man on the phone wanted an appointment. When Dad asked why, she said he wouldn't say and that he would only talk with him. Because so many people approached Dad asking for cash, he almost turned down this request, but something changed his mind. He set an appointment for that afternoon."

Bob then picked up the narrative. "Two o'clock sharp, there was a knock at Dad's office door. Mrs. Price led in Professor Archenhold, a short, stooped man of about seventy with bright, intelligent eyes and wearing a well-worn brown-and-gray tweed suit, old, scuffed, brown shoes, and a faded brown hat atop a mass of gray-streaked black hair. Dad said he wasn't much to look at, but he had undefinable magic. The professor removed an untidy two inches of papers from a worn and battered leather briefcase. Then he looked Dad directly in the eye and, in a heavy German accent, asked, 'Do you believe in time travel?'"

Paul leaned forward. "You have got to be kidding! What did your father say?"

William smiled, "He asked Doctor Archenhold if he preferred tea or coffee."

"No way!" said Ellie.

Bob laughed. "Way. Tea. He told Dad he had been a physicist in Germany before World War Two, but as he was Jewish, he had to flee the country in 1937. He and several colleagues had been working on the atomic bomb and stumbled onto some strange equations that led them to believe time travel was theoretically possible. After arriving in America, he became an instructor at a small eastern college and didn't look at his previous work for years. After the war, he went back to it, slowly and laboriously refining the equations. I don't understand the dynamics as well as William does."

William shifted on the sofa and smiled at his brother, "Thanks a lot, you left the heavy lifting for me. No, I probably can't explain it better than you, but I'll repeat what little I've read from Dad's notes and some of Doctor Archenhold's old notes. I think Doctor Archenhold wrote some of his notes trying to simplify it for Dad. Albert Einstein wrote that *time* was an illusion and not a constant. Scientists discussed things in terms of three dimensions. Those three are length, height, and width. Einstein added a fourth dimension, direction, which moves forward. His theory of special relativity says time speeds up and slows down. We are now talking about the bending of space-time. If you fly in a spaceship at the speed of light, which is 186,282 miles per second, you will age more slowly. Thus, time has been changed. Where I really get lost is wormholes. I think they are the secret to Doctor Archenhold's ability to time travel. I think the wormholes permitted speeds greater than the speed of light, so greater differences in space-time bending could be created. I think it's possible when we make a jump, it's through a wormhole. Ultimately, he was certain time travel was possible, but it would be an extremely expensive proposition."

"You're really serious about this?" asked Ellie.

"Yep. Completely serious. He and Dad started planning that night. It took years and millions of dollars, but it led to this place and a time machine."

"You are talking about a time machine?" she asked, incredulous.

"Right."

"Whatever happened to the other men who worked with Archenhold in Germany?" asked Ellie.

William rested his chin in the palm of his left hand. "Doctor Archenhold said he searched for his colleagues after the war but never found out what became of them. We can probably guess. Remember, he was Jewish."

"That is an amazing story!" interjected Paul. "Amazing!"

"I agree," said Bob. "We'll show you the rest of this place tomorrow. This is where William and I grew up. This is where they assembled the Wattson Timer. Be prepared."

"Let's get a good night's sleep. Bob and I will show you around in the morning. Your bedrooms are down this way," said William, pushing open a door and turning to the right. They followed him down a wide, carpeted corridor with doors every twenty feet on both sides.

William waved his arm.

"My and Bob's bedrooms are the last two on the left. The rooms are all about the same, so take whichever ones you like. They each have a bathroom. You can set the thermostat on the right-hand wall so that you're comfortable."

Ellie and Paul each chose a door and walked into their rooms. Ellie flipped on the light switch, pleasantly surprised at how comfortable her room appeared. On the light-tan walls were several oil paintings that looked vaguely familiar. Western art. The beige carpet was so thick she left footprints as she walked across it. There was a sofa covered in the same nubby, gray fabric as those in the viewing room, as well as a wood-frame chair with back and seat cushions covered in red-and-gray striped velvet. An ornately carved, dark wood, rectangular table sat between the chair and sofa. On this table was an old-fashioned lamp with a pull chain and heavy wood base and a tan, translucent shade painted with Western scenes. The double bedspread was bright Navaho geometric patterns of red, blue, and tan. Behind a sliding door, she found a small closet and, next to it, a door leading into the bathroom, which was all shiny chrome, glass, and white tile and a shower stall. The room did not feel lived in, and Ellie wondered if she was the first person to ever stay in it.

After looking over her bedroom, she knocked on Paul's door, stepped in, and found his room to be almost identical to hers. They were both pleased with how comfortable their rooms were. They were the nicest bedrooms either friend had ever had.

Bob soon knocked on Paul and Ellie's doors, told them about the alarm clocks on their nightstands, and asked them to meet him and William in the hallway at 8:00 a.m.

"I'm in the last room to the left. Let me know if you need anything during the night. It's been a long day."

Bob was right about the long day. Soon, they all showered and, finding pajamas in their dressers, went to bed. The rooms had no televisions, so reading was the sleep aid of choice.

The next morning, everyone was up, refreshed, outside their rooms promptly at eight, and reported no nightmares. Paul and Ellie wore the same clothes as the day before while Bob and William wore gray jumpsuits. As William had mentioned the night before, from here on, they would be provided clothes for their trip.

With a big smile on his face, William said, "Follow me and let's get you in the proper attire."

He followed the hall to another unmarked door, pushed down a metal door handle, and walked into a dark room. He flipped on the lights, and they found themselves in a large, square storage room, fifty feet long on a side. The room was brightly lit even though several of the bulbs had burned out. It looked like an abandoned department store storage room. Dozens of gray jumpsuits hung on racks down the room's right-hand wall. Each suit's left breast pocket was embroidered with a bright, multicolored emblem, and the back of each suit sported three horizontal, blue stripes. Stacks of shoe boxes and a wooden bench were on the left side of the room.

"Okay, let's get everyone outfitted," William said as he and Bob walked over to the jumpsuits. They helped the others choose the correct sizes by guessing as well as by holding them up to each person. William said Bob's size looked like a circus tent. Zippers ran down the front and the lower outside pants leg of each suit, making it easy to slip them over their regular clothes. They soon stared in a mirror and remarked how good they looked.

"Why did your dad have all these suits?" asked Ellie.

Bob said, "The suits have sensors that allow you to move throughout the building without setting off alarms. Also, a central console tracks each person's movements. Dad didn't want anyone who wasn't supposed to be here to get inside and wander around. Most of these were for workers finishing projects and final detail work after the system was up and running."

The friends then moved across the room to the stack of shoeboxes, where they found heavy canvas black shoes with thick, rubber soles and round, black laces. This fitting was easier because everyone knew their shoe size. They had to do a little searching to find a pair of size sixes for Ellie, but find them they did at the bottom of the stack. Both Paul and Ellie remarked how comfortable they were. They dropped their old ones into the empty shoeboxes.

"Bob, what is this emblem on the pocket?" Ellie asked.

"It's a starburst with the Timer breaking through the center."

"It's hard to tell what it is," she replied.

"You really can't tell what it represents, and Dad wanted it that way. He didn't exactly want to advertise what he was able to do."

"Okay, you, two, go change and let's have some breakfast. I'm starving," Bob said as the others laughed. This was no surprise.

Their shoeboxes under their arms and their jumpsuits thrown over their shoulders, Paul and Ellie went to their rooms and changed, and then everyone met again in the hall. All but Bob remarked how comfortable their new outfits were. He thought his had possibly shrunk a little since the last time he wore it.

"Bob wears Dad's old suits," said William with a wistful tone. "I wonder if they have shrunk as well?"

They followed Bob into a series of rooms, an area he called the residential suite. The rooms were smaller, the ceilings lower, and the furniture and decorations much more in keeping with a home. Bob said his father had not decorated this area but instead had taken the plans to Denver where an interior designer chose items and shipped them to him. She did this based on a set of blueprints and had no idea that it was essentially a cave.

The last room was larger, with a free-standing rock fireplace open on both sides and dividing a sitting room and combination kitchen/dining area. A wood fire burned merrily.

"What pretty rocks these are," remarked Ellie as she bent down to look at them more closely.

William walked to her side. "Can you tell what those shiny streaks are?"

"They just look like shiny streaks to me," she replied.

"These rocks are striated with gold. Dad owned several abandoned gold mines. Originally, the miners left columns of rock to hold up the ceilings, and many of the columns had gold veins running through them. Dad cleaned up the tailings on the outside and sealed the mines with heavy metal sheets. When practical, he even had trees planted to conceal the entrances. When he built this place, he sent men back to several of the structurally safe mines and had them shore up the ceilings and remove some of the columns, and he chipped these rocks from them. He also used some column remnants in other places. Check out some of the doorstops and paperweights, for instance."

"Amazing!" responded Ellie as she leaned forward to get a closer look at a large cornerstone.

On the sitting room side, a round glass-topped coffee table separated dark-brown leather chairs and tan leather sofas. Persian rugs covered the floor. Numerous watercolor and oil paintings lent an artist's studio vibe.

Paul ran his hand over a plush rug "I guess these are the real thing?"

William smiled and replied, "The real thing and from a very long time ago."

A gleaming, stainless steel modern kitchen dominated the other side, along with a huge, round, dark-oak dining table with ten matching captain's chairs.

"Dad didn't like rectangular tables. He said the person at the other end might just as well be in another room," added William. "He liked everyone to look into the eyes of the person he was talking with."

Dailey Jones was bending over the stove and looked around when they walked in. "Come on, over, guys, it's almost ready."

He then filled cream-colored platters with scrambled eggs and hash browns. He had already placed two platters of crisp bacon on the table, and he removed a tray of buttered wheat toast from one of the ovens.

Bob looked at all the food. "Nothing smells better than bacon and toast!"

Dailey laughed and said, "There's milk and orange juice in the refrigerator and cereal if anyone wants any." His spread did not put anyone in the mind for cereal.

William and Bob took drink orders and poured milk and juice into tall, green glasses. They set the glasses on the table, and everyone but Dailey sat down. He sipped coffee and said he had already eaten.

"Mr. Jones, this is wonderful!" Ellie said, beaming with pleasure.

"Young lady, everyone calls me Dailey, and I want you to do the same. And thanks."

"Well, Dailey, it is wonderful," repeated Ellie.

"And yummy too, Dailey," said Bob with a grin, which earned him a poke in the ribs from Ellie.

They all had great appetites, and soon the mountain of food disappeared. Bob remarked how much he had missed Dailey's cooking and also complimented him on the excellent honey as he poured some over a piece of toast.

Finally, William stood up. "Let's clean up the kitchen and then make a decision."

"What decision?" Paul asked.

"Does everyone want to see the Wattson Timer? It kind of leads into why we came out here this summer."

"The Wattson Timer?" asked Paul.

"Right."

"I vote we go right now," said Ellie.

Everyone pitched in, and the kitchen soon sparkled. Paul and Ellie were excited to see the Wattson Timer.

"Right this way, follow me," William said. The door on the opposite wall opened to a long corridor with a familiar metal-grated floor.

"Without these jumpsuits, this grate would retract, and we would drop to the bottom of this shaft," William said.

"A long drop," added Bob sardonically.

CHAPTER 5

THE TIMER

THE GROUP FOLLOWED William down a long corridor that ended in thirty feet of metal grating. Crossing the grate, William pushed open a heavy, metal door.

"Why no buttons, William? This is the first main door we've seen without them," Paul asked.

"I guess Dad figured if anyone got this far, one more combination lock wouldn't stop them." He stepped through the door and flipped a light switch.

The room they entered was square, eighty feet on a side and twenty feet high, and with stark-white floor, ceiling, and walls. Mesh-covered openings were scattered every fifteen feet along each of the walls. William said that these were air filters to keep the atmosphere as dust-free as possible. Three rows of recessed lights illuminated the room: one down the center and the other two twenty feet to each side. A thirty-foot red circle dominated the floor's center, and in the middle of the circle stood the Wattson Timer.

Ellie immediately said it looked like a flying saucer. Its four stubby legs each ended in a square foot at the end of a hydraulic cylinder that slid into the leg. Bob said these legs kept the Timer as level as possible and supported a disk thirty feet across. The disk tapered from six feet thick at the outer edge to twelve feet thick at the center. The outside ten feet of the saucer's surface was a gleaming, burnished copper band while the rest was painted matte gray. Around the upper decks outside edge ran a low railing broken only for a black metal ladder, extending almost to the floor.

Following Bob, they climbed to the Timer's flat top. Paul and Ellie were very quiet. In the top deck's middle, a step led down into the cockpit, which was seven feet across and three feet deep and had two black leather seats. One seat faced an odd-looking set of controls, primarily buttons and colored lights. Behind the seats was an open hatchway. A round hatch with a circular wheel and locking mechanism in its base leaned back against the side of the cockpit.

William sat in the left seat, bent forward, and pushed a series of buttons. The instrument panel lit up with green, blue, and red lights.

"It looks complicated, but it really isn't," he said.

The lights were grouped by color: a cluster of green on the left, red on the right, and blue in the center. There was a figure-eight-shaped steering yoke in front of the left-hand seat, and between the seats, set in the floor, was a gear shifter topped with a circular brass knob. William said it controlled the Timer's speed. There were floor pedals in front of both seats. William pushed several buttons, turning off the dashboard lights.

"Come on and see what's inside," Bob said as he motioned Ellie and Paul onto a ladder at the top of the hatchway.

All four climbed down the ladder. The interior looked like the inside of a yacht hull with two sets of bunk beds aligned with the curved wall along one side. A small kitchen was built into the wall, adjacent to the beds. Next to the little kitchen, a black leather sofa had been curved to fit into the wall. It faced two low-back, black-cushioned chairs bolted to the floor. Storage bins covered with netting lined the opposite side. More cabinets, these with latched doors, were built into the wall, and the floor was slightly lower in the center, affording more headroom. The wood trim and cabinet doors were varnished, and all metal was painted a light green. All in all, it was tight but comfortable and efficiently designed.

"Watch this," said Bob as he walked over to the only empty section wall. He pulled a handle, and the wall rolled toward him and revealed seats like the ones on the upper deck, with a set of controls and a yoke in front of the left seat. A small screen, set in the wall's center, faced the seat's front.

"You can drive the Timer from in here. It wasn't in the original plans. Dad added it later. You can control the view on the screen to a limited degree. It's not as good as driving from the top, but he said it was a good backup."

"I think this is all pretty amazing! When was it designed and built?" Ellie inquired.

"Dad put the project together a long time ago. Pretty modern-looking for something that's almost fifty years old, don't you think?" said William.

"Some of the optics and navigation equipment were upgraded over the years, but the Timer is the same as the day they completed it." With that, he climbed up the ladder and through the hatch to the top deck.

The others followed him to the top and then down the outside ladder. They stood on the floor at the base, Paul and Ellie facing the brothers.

Ellie reached over, grasped William's wrist, and pulled him toward her until they were face-to-face. "William, why are you showing us all this?"

William reached over with his free arm and placed it around Ellie shoulders. "Come on and let's go talk about it," and he led them across the floor.

He pushed open a heavy metal door, and they walked into a book-filled room. The books, mostly leather-bound with gold-embossed spines and gilded text block, were lined up neatly, each spine perfectly aligned with each shelf edge.

William said that his dad loved to read and kept every book. "He loved beautiful, leather-covered, gold-embossed, AEG books."

"What's an AEG book?" asked Paul.

"Oh, sorry, Paul. AEG is 'all edges gold.'"

"Well, that's okay, I like those as well. I don't have any, but I like them anyway."

"Who is this in the photograph?" Ellie asked as she pointed to an 8×10 framed photo on the top shelf. It showed an attractive lady with curly, gray hair and frank gray eyes. There was a signed and dated inscription. The only intelligible letter of the signature was an A at the beginning of the first name.

William answered after a glance at the photo. "That's Amelia Earhart. She was a friend of Dad's."

Ellie looked closer. "The date is July 5, 1950. I thought she disappeared and was declared dead in absentia in the 1930s?"

"Well, I guess they were wrong," William said with a knowing smile.

Dark mahogany tables were next to chairs and topped by banker's lamps with sparkling green glass shades. The light shining through the colored glass cast a warm glow in an otherwise somber room. Comfortable, brown leather chairs surrounded two oxblood-colored leather sofas. William lowered himself into one of the chairs and propped his feet on a marble-topped coffee table, also mahogany.

Paul leaned over the coffee table and peered at it. "What's this carved into the top, William?"

"That's our family crest."

Giving William a puzzled look, Paul said, "But it has only one 'T,' why?"

"When my great-grandfather came through Ellis Island, they asked his name and how to spell it. He stuttered, so they spelled it with two Ts. After he discovered the error, he decided he didn't want to go back through the line. It didn't bother Dad. He said he kind of liked it being a little different.

"Okay, enough of that. Everyone, grab a seat. The Park Service says that to travel Yellowstone's bear country, you should be in a party of at least four. Basically, Bob and I are going to travel bear country, and we don't want the bears to get us."

"What kind of travel?" Paul asked.

"I hope you're ready for this, and I really don't blame you if you're not. We are thinking about time travel. Bob and I have decided to do it. We felt we needed more than the two of us. Safety in numbers, you know. That is where the Wattson Timer comes in."

"Seriously? Can you really do it? Why take us and not Dailey?"

Bob leaned forward, placing his hands on his knees. "Dailey has had some health issues that might come into play when we're a long way from a doctor. Secondly, you two fit what we are looking for."

"What's that?" asked Paul.

"My turn," said William. "We don't have any other close friends or relatives. Dailey is all we've got. You're just like us. Nobody is going to come looking for you if you're gone for two or three months. We should be back well before the fall semester starts, and you won't miss any of the regular session or activities before school starts."

Paul looked over at Bob. "We'd better not miss the start of football practice or Coach Summers will have our hides."

"You're both athletic and have outdoor experience and both are needed. Also, you're both smart. There is no good substitute for common sense."

"And mainly, you're our best friends, and we like and trust you both," interjected Bob.

"William, what if we decide not to do it?" asked Paul.

"You walk out of here tomorrow and no questions asked. Bob and I will go on our own, and you fly back. We've been thinking about this for a long time. We think you would keep quiet about this place."

"You will miss out on adventures and experiences most people can only imagine," added Bob.

William smiled and said, "Or adventures and experiences most people can't imagine. We may see things that no longer exist and maybe even see history in the making. Really, we don't know what to expect or what we will see, but I would hate for you to miss it."

Paul reached out his hand to William. "Okay, I'm in."

Ellie placed her hand over theirs. "Me too!"

Bob placed his large hand over Ellie's small one. "Yea! Me three! I am excited!"

William leaned back and, with a thoughtful expression, said, "Okay. Now, let's go over a few things. There will be danger involved. Hopefully not much, but we would be foolish to think there would be none. We have some things to train with that I think will minimize it, but there will probably be some. You won't be able to contact anyone for the two to three months we're gone. If you're like I am, that will be no big deal. If someone gets injured, we will have to handle the initial treatment. There will be no doctors around the corner. If we forget something, whether it's food or Bob, there is no coming back for it. We'll have to plan carefully."

Bob placed both palms down flat on the coffee table and leaned forward. "And no matter what, nobody gets left behind."

"That thought never entered my mind," Paul said as he high-fived Bob.

William continued, "I know you had wanted to work this summer and earn some money, so maybe Bob and I can try to help with that."

Paul laughed and said, "Since I have never had any money, it won't have to be much to make me happy."

"Same here, but, guys, you really don't have to do that for me. If I had any money, I would pay you to take me," said Ellie.

"That's what makes it so special to me and William. We'll see what we can do. Remember, it may be dangerous. No, it probably *will* be dangerous, but think of the things we'll see." Bob held out his hand to Ellie, palm up.

"Well, I'm not scared. I'd just like to see something the four of us couldn't handle," said Ellie with a grin as she stood and gave Bob's big hand a hard slap.

William turned sideways and hung his legs over one arm of the chair. "Big decisions, where do we go and in what time period? Bob, tell Ellie and Paul what we've been thinking about. We want to make sure everyone is on board."

"Well, keeping in mind we can go anywhere, how about four hundred miles north of here?"

"Montana?" asked Paul.

"Yep, there and part of Wyoming as well. William and I are familiar with a good bit of that area, though I suspect it's changed a little in the last two hundred years."

"What time period are you thinking about, Bob?" asked Ellie.

"William and I thought 1805 would be a good year."

"Why 1805?"

"Isn't that about the time of the Lewis and Clark Expedition?" questioned Paul.

"You get an 'A,'" said William. "Lewis and Clark got to Montana in April of 1805. They spent the next seven months traveling across the state."

"Seven months seems like a long time to travel across a state," said Paul.

Bob settled back on one of the sofas. "It is a long time, but Montana is the fourth largest state, and it's a long state. Probably eight hundred miles at its widest if you go straight across. Plus, they traveled in slow boats and had to get around waterfalls. In some places, they pulled the boats over land for miles. They recorded all kinds of information for President Jefferson. It would have taken a while. I think Dad came up with some of Meriwether Lewis's original notes. Don't really know how."

"Do you think we'll be able to see the expedition?" asked Ellie.

"We might try to see them without them seeing us. Montana is wide open in lots of places, but it's also full of rolling hills. We should be able to easily hide the Timer behind a crest. We'll have to be in the right place at the right time. They kept detailed records, so it shouldn't be that hard if we're patient and study a little."

William swung one foot to the floor.

"Bob and I thought we might travel at night when it's necessary. We will be following rivers, so it shouldn't be too hard to keep up with where we are. The rivers will have changed course somewhat but will generally be the same. Also, waterfalls will give us an idea of our location. No GPS, but we can use a compass."

Paul put his hands behind his head and leaned back. "How fast and high will the Timer go? How long will it stay charged?"

"The Timer moves low and slow. Top speed is probably twenty miles an hour, and it will hover twelve to fifteen feet off the ground. If you ran it off a fifty-foot cliff, it wouldn't hit the ground. It would start slowing as it dropped, but it would still give you a good jolt. That's what Dailey says. Thankfully, we've never run it off a fifty-foot cliff. It will go months off a single charging. Maybe that's what Dad had in mind, limit its capabilities but don't use up the charge. Bob and I aren't sure why it's so limited, but it is."

"I think William is right. Less speed, more time at the location," added Bob.

"Bob and I thought everyone might like to see one of the huge buffalo herds up in Montana and what Yellowstone looked like two hundred years ago. I want to see some of the geysers that were active back then but have now shut down. I want to see what Wyoming and Montana looked like without people."

"And Idaho as well, William."

"Bob's right. We'll probably drift into eastern Idaho."

Ellie clapped her hands. "Gosh, it does sound great!"

"What do we need to do to get ready?" asked Paul.

"There are several things we need to do. Bob and I thought about period clothes, but now we think the best thing to do is just avoid people and not be seen. It would be difficult to explain just what and who we are. We need food for six to eight weeks. We need to train you both to fly the Timer should something happen to us or if we get lost. Two drivers out of four people just doesn't make sense. We need to have backups."

"You better not get lost!" Paul said.

"We don't intend to," William said, laughing at Paul. "But you never know. We also need to train you with our weapons."

Ellie sat up straight. "We have weapons?"

"We have nonlethal pneumatic dart guns, but they can kill," said William, pointing his right index finger like a gun.

"How can they be nonlethal but still kill?" she asked, with a puzzled expression.

"We have handguns that can fire five darts and long guns that can fire ten. One dart will drop a man in his tracks, but more than two can be dangerous. Four or five will stop a bear in thirty seconds, but that might make for a mighty long thirty seconds. Just remember, if you fire at a bear, make sure you stay away until the darts take him to the ground. Even then, be careful."

Paul shook his head. "The darts sound pretty dangerous."

Bob chimed in, "Not really as long as we don't shoot each other. The needles stay enclosed in the shell until they exit. As they leave the barrel, the needle runs out and helps keep the trajectory true. You just need to be mindful of where you aim."

"What's the range?" asked Paul.

"The long guns have about a fifty-yard range but aren't very accurate at that distance. The pistols…maybe thirty. You'll get used to them after a little practice."

"Trust me, I want to practice," said Paul. "If a bear is coming after me, I don't want to miss."

"You won't miss," said William. "Bob is a really good instructor and a great shot."

"Where in Montana will we start?" asked Ellie.

"Bob and I studied both old and new maps. Tell me how this sounds. We are thinking about landing near the Missouri River at its junction with the Musselshell River. The Missouri is a perfect guide to follow west. We may see buffalo herds, Indians, the Lewis and Clark Expedition…who knows what we'll see? Bob, let's use your iPad and show them what we're planning," William said, pulling the coffee table closer.

Bob got an iPad out of a drawer and handed it to William. Then he took a bag of chocolate chip cookies from the same drawer. "Forgot these were in there." And he popped a cookie into his mouth.

William laid the iPad on the coffee table and opened it to a map showing the entire state of Montana. He placed his right index finger on the map. "The Musselshell River joins the Missouri right here. It's about one hundred miles east and thirty miles north of Lewistown."

His finger then traced across Montana. "We follow the Missouri several hundred miles to a point about halfway between Butte and Bozeman." He let his finger now slide farther south down the map. "We pick up the Madison River and follow it into Idaho and to the southwest corner of Yellowstone. There, we jump to the Bechler River and follow it into the heart of Yellowstone. That's the plan so far. We'll have to think a bit about what to do in the park."

"Do you follow the rivers for direction?" asked Paul.

"Not just for direction although that's a big help. Traveling across the plains is not an issue, but once you get into a forest and can't climb higher than twenty feet, it can be a big problem. It's a way of traveling across country by the easiest path we can find. We need to be aware of waterfalls as high ones can make us turn back or go around. Bob and I are pretty much up on the waterfalls in Yellowstone and on the Missouri, but there may be some we don't know about. A lot can change in two hundred years."

Ellie ran her fingers back through her hair. "I think it will be great following the rivers. Wildlife watching and waterfalls are two things I really like. Wildlife tends to congregate along rivers, and waterfalls are always on rivers or streams."

"I feel the same way," said William. "Bob and I have hiked to dozens of falls throughout Yellowstone. I'm really looking forward to that part of the trip."

William stood up and stretched. "Okay, when we get to the Bechler, we can evaluate our supplies and time."

"Supplies? Meaning food?" asked Bob with a studied look on his face.

"Pretty much but also other things like medical supplies. I hope nothing causes us to run short of those. And we need to make sure the Timer's power isn't a problem. I talked with Dailey, and he said there should be way more than we need. I don't think time will come into play unless it takes much longer to get to the Bechler than I've planned. I don't think it will."

"If I understand what you're saying," said Paul, "we can stay as long as we have time and resources. I like the sound of that."

"I vote to go as planned. I know this, I'm really, really excited!" said Ellie, playfully punching Bob's broad back.

"Me too!" added Paul, standing and thrusting his arms into the air.

"Great! That sounds good to me!" said William.

Bob stood up and rubbed his stomach. "Okay, great for me too. Let's go eat some lunch."

The others laughed, and then they all walked across the white floor, through the door, and back to the kitchen area.

Dailey had been frying chicken, mashing potatoes, and baking biscuits. He took a fresh salad out of the refrigerator and began laying out the food. The chicken was crisp and golden, the potatoes creamy white, and the biscuits domed on top with flat, crusty brown bottoms.

As usual, Bob and William took drink orders while Ellie and Paul set the table. When Ellie remarked on the pretty pitchers, William said, "Let's take a look at one of them."

He lifted one and pointed to the word "Revere" inside a rectangle.

"Wow! Is it real?" whispered Ellie.

"It's as real as can be."

As he poured honey over a biscuit, Bob said, "Boy, I have really missed your cooking, Dailey."

"I thought you looked a little thin when I picked you up in Jackson. I decided to fix your favorite meal. And banana pudding for dessert."

"Dailey, I haven't looked thin since the second grade, but if it's the thought that counts, I appreciate it."

As Dailey said, they went through all the food like General Sherman through Georgia and finished it off with bowls of banana pudding.

Dailey beamed at all the praise and said, "Soup and sandwiches tonight."

CHAPTER 6

PREPARING TO LEAVE

THE NEXT MORNING, everyone got up early and enjoyed another of Dailey's excellent breakfasts. They even introduced Paul to grits. He eyed them suspiciously but took a cautious bite. Pronouncing them edible, he proceeded to have two helpings.

Ellie, finishing a much smaller portion of grits, leaned her elbows on the table, cupped her chin in her hands, and asked William, "How in the world did your father manage to build this fantastic place and how did he keep it secret?"

After taking a long swallow of milk, William began, "Well, it's kind of a long story. The first thing Dad did was set up a company to handle the construction. He filtered everything through it. Then he had a Denver architectural firm draw up plans, which he forwarded to a large engineering firm. As almost all the construction was in solid rock, location didn't really matter. Everything had to be blasted or hammered out. He contacted a friend in the mining business who recommended a construction superintendent, Mr. McGeorge, and said he was the best in the business. Dad bought him a house out by the highway. He and his wife moved in a month later. He helped Dad hire out-of-state and out-of-work hard-rock miners. As they finalized the plans, the superintendent placed several huge orders of equipment. Dad said it took some massive checks to cover them. The equipment was delivered at the main road five miles away and then transported to a warehouse Dad had built at the mountain's base."

"Now, the hardest part was the miners," added Bob. "They had to hire seventy-five of them. This wasn't difficult because it was a slow time in the mining business. They screened more than twice that many to get the ones they needed. They selected them carefully and tried, especially, to hire those with families who were having a hard time. Many came from Nevada and Montana and some from Colorado. The ones that didn't live in Colorado flew to Denver at company expense. They stayed in a hotel for several days until everyone arrived. When they all got to Denver, buses with blacked-out windows brought them to this building site. By then, an Idaho construction firm had built a wooden dorm. For the next year and a half, there was around-the-clock blasting, jackhammering, hauling, and erecting. Dad said he felt safe in saying that for eighteen months, these were the best-paid miners in the US."

"By the way," William chimed in, "after finishing Dad's project, many of these guys went to work for his friend who owned a company that specialized in deep mining."

"Right," agreed Bob. "As the construction progressed, additional items like elevators, steel doors, and catwalks were delivered and installed. When they completed that construction, carpenters came to the site under the same secrecy as the miners, who by then had returned home with their pockets full of money, including very large bonuses. Then carpenters converted the large, bare rooms into bedrooms, baths, the kitchen, and common areas like the library and gym. This is when they delivered the kitchen equipment and a good bit of the furniture."

William then took over again, continuing the brothers' story. "Dad flew artisans in from Italy to build some of the furniture, like this coffee table. I think the tabletop came from an Italian palace. Those fellows also did some of the stonework you see around here, like the fireplace in the kitchen. Also, they installed the gemstones into the steps during this phase. Dad and Dailey were particularly watchful while they did this."

"Okay," said Bob. "The work was now almost complete. They'd installed the surveillance and security equipment. They brought heating and cooling units to the mountain and put them in place, but not too much heating or cooling has ever been needed. Temperature in here is a constant seventy to seventy-five degrees. As with the miners and carpenters, the companies doing this worked under tight security. Except for some wiring and plumbing, the work was finished."

"Almost all the work," said William. "Dad referred to this phase as 'covering his tracks.' He had all the buildings near the road torn down, slabs broken up and carried away, and power lines coming into these buildings removed. It was as if none of it had ever existed."

Paul steepled his fingers. "William, how is this place powered?"

"Initially, completely with generators but now also with solar. We still have backup generators run by natural gas, which Wyoming has in abundance. But we use those only as needed."

"Whew, bet this place was expensive to build," said Ellie, rolling her eyes.

"A fortune, but Dad had several fortunes," replied Bob.

"I can see there was lots of secrecy, but what about the superintendent?" she inquired.

Bob smiled. "Mr. McGeorge is still on the payroll, listed as a consultant. He helped William and me several times with things involving this place. Mr. and Mrs. McGeorge are living a very comfortable retirement up in Montana."

"Dad made sure Bob and I knew he is to be paid as long as he and Mrs. McGeorge live. Dad said he was probably the one indispensable person in the entire project. He got the main construction completed and kept seventy-five men relatively happy for eighteen months. I bet that wasn't easy."

"No, I bet not," replied Paul. "That's a long time to be away from your family."

Bob smiled again. "Dad thought about that. He shut down operations a week at Christmas, and each man got another week off during the year. He also sent them home each of those weeks with extra money in their pockets."

"I bet they hated to see this job end," said Ellie.

"Well, the mining industry had recovered from a two-year slump and was booming again when they finished here. I think they were okay," said Bob.

CHAPTER 7

TRAINING

"WHEN ARE WE going to get to shoot the guns?" asked Ellie.

"I say let's go to the armory now," Bob answered. "William and I can show you how to defend yourself against grizzly bears and villains. Lead the way, brother."

They followed William down the hall to the last door on the right, which he pushed open. They stepped into a long, low room that had been blasted out of the native rock, a room roughly seventy-five feet long by thirty feet wide and eight feet high. It was pleasantly cool even though there were no air vents. They saw racks of what looked like toy pistols and long guns on their left, and starting on the right and at ever-increasing distances, round targets hanging from the ceiling, with mesh aprons was around each target's perimeter. At each target's base was a rectangular, plastic catch basin. The targets, composed of white foam material, had two-inch-wide black bands drawn an inch outside a red five-inch circular bull's-eye.

William and Bob walked over to a rack and removed two odd-looking weapons that looked almost like water guns. These "pistols" were plastic with a bulb at the base of each butt. The boys walked over to a heavy wood table in the back of the room. After verifying they were not ready to fire, they quickly and expertly disassembled them. The guns were easy to reassemble because there were not many parts.

"These are made of a composite plastic that's almost unbreak-able. The barrel and the firing mechanism contain the only metal. We had to do some work to make the feed from the clips smooth, but it seems to be fine," said William.

Bob turned his pistol over in his hand, indicating the bulb on the butt, and said, "This holds the compressed air that fires the darts. The Timer has two charging stations, so we can keep them ready to use."

William added, "The pistols and long guns both have iron or open sights but can be fitted with laser attachments. They pretty much shoot where the red dot shines."

Ellie and Paul now tried what they had just watched. While not as fast as William and Bob, after a few minutes and a little instruc-tion, they had taken apart and reassembled the guns several times.

Bob walked over to a cabinet and removed some shiny, metal, cylindrical darts, explaining that though they were duds, they were filled with enough water to simulate the real thing.

"We decided to start training you with the pistols because they're more difficult to master." He stretched out a handful of the darts to his brother. Each removed a clip from just in front of the trigger guard and loaded it then slapped their clips back into place. They locked with audible clicks.

"Keep it pointed down range," said Bob as he handed his gun to Paul.

Paul hefted it in his hand, surprised at the weight. "It sure is light. How does it work?"

As if to answer, Bob reached over and took the gun from Paul's hand and walked to the firing line.

"No need for ear protection when someone shoots these guns, it's almost like they have silencers."

"Watch Bob," said his brother. "He's the gunnery sergeant around here."

Bob took a shooter's stance, with one foot slightly in front of the other and both hands on the gun. He raised his arms to eye level and, in rapid succession, fired five shots. Each shot made a quiet pop as a dart flew out of the barrel and hurled toward the target thirty feet away. All five darts were within the outer black circle, four of them in the red bull's-eye as the target swayed very slightly.

"Not too bad, considering Bob hasn't practiced in nearly six months."

"I'm a little rusty, but it'll come back to me," Bob said, pretending to blow the smoke off the end of the barrel.

"Did you say a little rusty? That was amazing!" said a smiling and impressed Ellie.

"I'll say!" added Paul as he looked on in wonder.

"Bob is better than I am, but with practice, you and Ellie will be able to do the same thing. Or better."

"Or better?" said Bob, a mischievous look on his face.

"Can I try?" asked Paul.

William handed his pistol to Paul. "Bob's a great shot. Listen to his instructions, and you will both be experts in no time."

After going over all the safety measures, Bob began the shooting instructions. He started with foot placement and trying for a stable shooting platform, if possible. He then moved to lining up the sights. This consisted of lining up the square front sight in the center of the square rear U-shaped sight and even with the top of each "U" arm. Then there was the push and pull of the hands on the gun—which hand aimed and which one carried the weight. He was very good at explaining the method in a way they understood.

"Why do we have to worry about the sights if we have the laser?" asked Ellie.

"What if something happened to the laser or it's broken?"

"I hadn't thought about that, good point," said Ellie, slightly nodding.

After firing twenty rounds each at the closest target, Paul and Ellie made rapid progress. They certainly didn't hit the bull's-eye every time, but they began to at least hit the target itself with all their shots.

William and Bob each got a pistol and began firing at the more distant targets. They were quickly hitting the bull's-eye with regularity, occasionally driving one dart into the butt of one previously fired.

Over the next hour, Ellie and Paul worked their way out to the target that was fifteen yards away. Out of every five shots, they were putting two to three darts into the bull's-eye. On his last clip of the day, Paul put four in the bull's-eye. Bob proclaimed them both naturals and said they would do this every day until they left.

"Just keep practicing," advised William. "You're both improving with every shot."

As Paul and Ellie put away their guns, William walked over to a third cabinet and came back with a knife in each hand.

"What are those for?" asked Paul.

William's answer was to take the knife in his right hand by its blade tip, draw it back just past his ear, and hurl it down the room. The knife whirled at a four-by-four-foot wooden target suspended from the ceiling by two three-foot chains. One inch of the blade drove into the wood, and the quivering knife stood in the center of a three-inch red circle. Almost too fast to see, he drew back the other knife and buried its point within an inch of the first one.

"That was unreal!" exclaimed Paul.

"I can sometimes outshoot him," said Bob, "but nobody is better throwing a knife than my brother. These are SOG throwing knives, and we've practiced with them for years."

Bob then took two knives and threw them within six inches of William's.

Ellie folded her arms across her chest. "You may not be as good as William, but you're pretty good."

"William, if we have guns, why do we need knives?" asked Paul.

"What if those guns are lost, stolen, lose their charge, the serum is no good, or they get broken? Two of those things don't happen to knives."

That made sense to Ellie and Paul, and they spent the next hour practicing under Bob and William's expert instruction. When they finished, they thought it would be a good idea to do this every day to get proficient. They found knife throwing to be more difficult than shooting. As neither Ellie nor Paul was left-handed, William suggested they practice throwing only right-handed because of the limited time available.

Thinking they had all done enough for the time being, William suggested they decide what they needed to do before departing on their adventure. They put away the guns and knives and left the armory.

The four friends sat around the kitchen table discussing their schedule for the next few weeks. William and Bob said they had decided there were two things everyone needed to master. The first was shooting reliably. The second was flying the Timer. They would devote the next two weeks to mastering both skills.

William said he hated to push them, but they needed to be able to drive the Timer proficiently. He wanted everyone to be familiar with its operation so that everyone could take over in case of injury. Dailey had instructed the brothers on numerous occasions but never outside. As Bob liked to say, they were adequate at best. As it turned out, Paul took to flying the Timer like it was second nature. He just seemed to have a knack for coordinating his hands and feet to make each movement smooth and easy.

An antiquated airplane yoke, which Bob said looked like deer antlers, steered the Timer. Two foot pedals controlled height; the left pedal caused the Timer to rise into the air, and the right dropped it back down.

William said that once you got used to using your hands and feet at the same time, it was not much more complicated than driving a car. You had to constantly be aware of height when learning to fly inside, but the pedals could be locked into place to assure steady height. He thought this would be a great asset while traveling over the vast distances of the American Great Plains.

Everyone took a turn at taking the Timer off the floor and maneuvering it around the room. William was careful to set the height pedal at three feet to keep anyone from hitting the ceiling and said they would let everyone drive once they got to Montana and were outside.

"I think then our skill level will pick up fast."

They all agreed Paul's skill level didn't need much improvement.

William asked Ellie to keep a running travel journal. He wanted a record of each day's activities, weather, and anything else that struck her fancy.

"Your handwriting is the only one of the four of us that anyone can read. You can be our Meriwether Lewis."

Stocking of the Timer was the last thing mentioned that afternoon. This would also have to start immediately. They began the laborious process of preparing a long list of needed supplies, meticulously keeping a master list. The supplies included, in part, food, water purifiers, sleeping bags and pads, medicine, clothes, and other assorted gear. Space was at a premium, so they would have to be careful to keep their wants and needs at about the same. There could be no going back for things lost, used up, or forgotten. It was decided there would be two lists. William maintained a secondary list of things they wanted to take but could do without if they ran out of room.

After the promised tomato soup and ham sandwiches that night, William suggested they take a ride. They stopped in the viewing room to make sure no one was around the main building's outside. William said that an alarm should have sounded had anyone been on the inside. They took the elevators down, with Ellie and Paul punching in the combinations they now knew. When they reached the ground floor, Bob walked over to a Jeep Wrangler and removed the canvas top, and then Paul and Ellie got into the back seat. William settled into the front passenger seat, and Bob got behind the wheel. He drove them out the double door as it rose toward the ceiling. Once outside, Bob pushed a button on the dashboard, and the door slid down and shut.

They drove out of the canyon and turned right toward the Gros Ventre Mountains, the Wind River Range of the Rocky Mountains looming behind them. Bob followed a rutted dirt road that led further into the foothills.

As they drove through a rough scrabble land of scrub trees, bushes, and scattered rocks, Ellie asked William where they were headed.

"Where you can't see lights, hear noise, or see people."

Bob steered the vehicle to the right, bounced up a steep, rutted road, and stopped on a small plateau. They could truly see for miles in every direction, with neither a light in sight nor a sound heard.

"Turn off the headlights, Bob," said William. "Now, look up, everyone."

Stars and a full moon illuminated the entire sky.

"Just look at the stars!" exclaimed Ellie.

"The sky is almost solid white with stars," added Paul.

William smiled and said, "If the moon wasn't so bright, you could really see them. I bet we get to see plenty of stars in 1805 Montana and Wyoming."

Paul and Ellie hadn't realized stars and quiet could be so enjoyable. William, being the group's astronomer, told them the names of various constellations and stars. After a while, they hopped back into the Wrangler and drove back to their station, deciding to drive into Jackson the next day to begin compiling supplies. Everyone was very quiet on the way back as if they were soaking up the magnificence of the starry heavens that seemed to form a canopy.

The next morning, after a pancake breakfast, they began compiling lists of things wanted and things needed. Bob immediately pointed out that, in his opinion, they had greatly underestimated the amount of sugar needed. William sighed but then agreed to a ten-pound increase.

"You will all thank me later," Bob said with a big smile.

After lunch, they drove into Jackson. Deciding to work on the food first, they parked at Smith's Food and Drugs and commandeered four shopping carts, soon piling them high with jerky, flour, salt, pepper, coffee, cooking oil, candy, nuts, dried fruit, and the not-to-be-forgotten sugar. They got a small supply of canned meats, stews, and soups after William said that cooking might be impossible at times, but maybe they could heat things. They pushed the overflowing carts to their dust-covered truck, unloaded them into the back, and covered everything with a heavy canvas tarp. Suddenly remembering powdered milk, Bob ran back inside and returned with several cases.

Their next stop was a specialty store for medical supplies. William chose an excellent emergency kit, and they added splints, more bandages, and a selection of medicines for every ailment they could think of. Fortunately, Ellie and William had taken an emergency medical course one summer although they were quick to admit their skills were cursory at best. They had volunteered as wilderness rangers, so most of what they had treated were sprains, small cuts, and poison ivy. They had also dealt with horseback-riding-related cracked ribs and one dislocated shoulder. As William said, "Bob and I are not to be confused with doctors."

Their last stop was on the town square at High Country Outfitters, one of Bob and William's favorite stores. They had been customers there for years. It specialized in the outdoor gear of every description. They pushed open the heavy, wood-front door, and William led them over to the shoe and boot department where he asked the sales assistant to outfit everyone with the best, most comfortable boots they had. This took a few minutes, but everyone was soon shod in new boots. Ellie requested a different color boot strings for hers and got them. With such a wide selection, everyone surprisingly chose some model of Vasque boots.

After teasing Ellie about the new boot strings, Bob said, "Let's all make sure we wear these each waking second for the next few weeks. We want to break them in as much as possible. Blisters are no fun for anyone."

William then filled a sack with new socks. They were various colors and ranged in size from Ellie's smalls to Bob's thirteen. Bob pulled out a bright, lime green pair of Ellie's.

"Ellie, if you don't like the color, feel free to change them for some new ones."

"Hush, Bob. You know I picked those out!" She giggled. "I'm just trying to add a little color to those drab, gray things you boys, chose."

Next, they walked upstairs where Bob bought a new R.L. Winston fly rod and some fly-making supplies. Everyone was getting hungry, so Bob suggested the Snake River Grill, one of the brothers' favorite local restaurants. They walked next door and up the stairs.

Bob said there were only two things he liked about the food: the quality and the quantity. After a short wait, they were led to their table, and menus were passed around.

"White tablecloths. Fancy!" said Ellie as she took in the log cabin walls, glowing fireplace, and metal fire screen with the restaurant's initials superimposed on its front.

"Okay, Bob, what are you going to get?" asked Paul as he scanned the menu.

"I think I shall have the dry-aged Kansas City sirloin with wild onion butter. I feel like a taste of beef tonight."

Paul also selected the sirloin steak, William the trout, and Ellie chose the poached tuna. After a wonderful meal topped off by rhubarb pie (Bob's selection, of course), they carried their bags of socks and canvass shoes out to their truck for the ride home. It started to rain, so they quickly put up the top and drove south, out of Jackson, after very a productive day.

The organizing, packing, and labeling started that night and continued for days. They checked items off the master list and stowed them on the Timer, each supply staying on the list until loaded and tucked. They were filling the usable storage space at an alarming rate. William pointed out the Timer was not designed for four people.

"Why four bunks then?" asked Paul.

"I don't know. We can ask Dailey if he knows."

He didn't.

Two days later, William and Dailey went back to Jackson and returned late afternoon with a large crate from Cabela's. It contained the crew's optics: four Zeiss Diafun 10×30 binoculars, a 20×60 Zeiss spotting scope and tripod, and four US night-vision binoculars with night-vision capabilities with headgear for hands-free use.

Peering at William through his night-vision binoculars, Paul asked, "What did all this cost? This is really good stuff."

"Oh, it's all paid for," William said in an unconcerned voice.

As everyone tried out their new gear, William reminded them at that "we want to see the other guy before he sees us. See, and not be seen."

CHAPTER 8

———————✦———————

LEAVING

TRAINING CONTINUED FOR ten more days, and everyone became more proficient with their weapons and flying the Timer. Bob and William's shooting and throwing were now superb. Ellie and Paul progressed past competent thanks to a combination of good coaching and steady practice. William said the secret was learning correctly from the start.

"Neither of you had any bad habits to break or unlearn. I heard once that practice doesn't make perfect, but perfect practice does."

Paul was now the best Timer driver. Bob and William had more experience, but Paul had a seemingly natural flair for controlling it, particularly at taking off and landing smoothly. He said it was from spending way too much time playing video games. Most importantly now, everyone could drive the Timer in an emergency.

With the storage cabinets almost full, they had worked out a system of tying things down with netting and now the netting bulged. They kept fragile items in the cabinets and put soft items and packaged items under the netting, which they were careful to secure as tightly as possible. They couldn't have things flying loose or rolling around on the floor.

They continued to think of things they needed. Bob pointed out that they would be gone for a good while. What if something happened to the water purifiers? What if they got separated from the Timer? They thought most of the water would be safe but not necessarily around camps or lots of animals. Bob made yet another trip to Jackson for canteens and some military-grade iodine water purification tablets, which came with taste-neutralizing tablets.

"I don't want anyone to catch giardia," he said, packing the new purchases away.

One day, Ellie looked up and said, "What about fire?"

Somehow, they had not thought about how to light their fires.

This time, William went back to Jackson and returned with a fire-starter kit consisting of a flint rod and a metal striker, two Zippo Windproof lighters with extra flints, lighter fluid, and a bag full of colorful plastic BIC lighters.

Finally, William spoke up during breakfast one morning. "Enough is enough. We need to set a date for takeoff. We could plan and pack forever. We're bound to forget something, but we should be good with what we have."

Their expressions seemed to combine trepidation with excitement. The thought of danger, mixed with uncertainty about the coming adventure, made their faces change by the second.

Ellie said what everyone was thinking, "Do you think it really works? I mean, can we really go back in time?"

William looked from face to face. "Yes, I do believe it. I think there is no one outside this place who would think that, but I do."

"Let's pick a day. How about one week from now?" William said, looking around the breakfast table.

A smile lit up Bob's face as he said, "I'm ready if you, guys, are. Let's do it a week from today."

They all nodded in agreement. Bob placed his large hand in the center of the table. William put his hand on top of Bob's, Paul's went on top of William's, and Ellie's small hand topped them all off. Then they settled back and finished their meals, each of them lost in thought.

The last week was frenzied, with all of them checking off items, packing, and tying down. They still needed a few things, such as sunglasses, and William got Ellie a watch with an altimeter.

"Who knows? We might need to know our altitude for some reason."

Finally, they were a day away. William glanced around the dinner table that night and said, "If we don't have it now, we haven't thought of it. If that's the case, we must not need it very badly. I say let's go. Everyone, get a good night's sleep. Let's meet at six in the morning for breakfast. And…it isn't too late to change your mind."

Then he stood and looked around the room. Each person nodded in assent as William's eyes went from one to another. With that, he walked out.

"Good night's sleep! I say fat chance of that." Bob chuckled.

Bob was correct. Nobody slept well that night, but they were all on time for breakfast the next morning. Dailey had cooked stacks of hotcakes with melted butter and warm syrup on the side and large platter of bacon. They chose from orange juice, coffee, and milk. Dailey looked over the four teenagers devouring the food and said, "I wanted you, guys, to have a good last meal."

With pancakes speared on his fork and poised at his mouth, Bob said, "You don't mean like condemned men, do you?"

"Sorry. I meant this is the last meal I'll fix you for a while. You know what I mean. You'll be cooking for yourselves, and I'm not sure how good that will be."

"Excellent point," replied Bob. Then he winked at Dailey and said, "I knew what you meant."

"Does everyone feel good and ready to go?" asked William.

Forks hit plates and heads turned toward William, their faces flushed with excitement. Bob took one last, long drink of milk.

"Just leave everything where it is. I'll clean up," said Dailey as the group stood up and filed past him. The boys shook his hand, and Ellie gave him a big hug. Dailey turned, and with a "Be careful," walked quickly out of the room. William thought he saw a tear in his old friend's eye.

Everyone dressed in the gray jumpsuits and hiking boots, and Bob and Paul wore caps from Teton Mountaineering, with ice axes embroidered across the fronts. They all walked into the large white room where the Timer sat waiting.

"I don't know about any of you, but my knees are shaking," said Ellie as she took a deep breath.

"Don't feel bad, Ellie, mine are too," William said, reaching over and squeezing her hand.

They walked to the Timer, and William stopped at the ladder's base, turned, and faced his friends. "This will be a big adventure. We need to remember every detail, one of us might write a book someday."

One by one, they climbed the rungs and dropped down to the interior, and the last one locked the hatch. William took the left-hand pilot's seat with his brother next to him, and they fastened their seat belts. Paul and Ellie took seats set into the wall and buckled in.

Bob turned in his seat. "Everyone make sure you're buckled in good. We've never done this before."

"As well as we really don't know exactly what to expect," added his brother.

"Okay, let's go," said William as he started flipping switches.

Green and red lights blinked on all over the console. Then they heard a light hum. He reached over, grasped a lever set in the center of the panel, and slowly pulled it down. They could feel a slight vibration. In a flash, the instrument panel and the screen were the only light visible. There was a jolt, and the screen went black. The Timer made a quarter turn to the left. Another jolt, and another quarter turn to the left, closely followed by the sensation of rising into the air and a loud pop. This caused the crew to catch their breath quickly. Suddenly, the screen in front of William and Bob lit up. It seemed to be covered with pink cotton candy, glistening. Illuminated.

"Wow!" exclaimed Bob.

The pink cotton film seemed to move up and out of the picture as if blown by a strong wind. Then it disappeared entirely. After another pop, not as loud as the first, the vibration stopped.

"Did we go anywhere William?" asked Paul.

"I really don't know. It didn't feel like it, but I guess we can find out." He unfastened his harness, swiveled his chair, and stood up. To relieve the tension, he reached over and tipped his brother's cap down over his eyes.

Ellie spoke up, "William, open up the hatch and let's see what the air smelled like two hundred years ago. I believe we have gone somewhere."

William turned off all the switches. Stepping to the ladder and raising himself on the lower rungs, he spun the locking mechanism and pushed the hatch up and out of his way and climbed out.

After a few seconds, he reappeared in the hatch opening.

"Come on up and have a look. Don't look up until you're out on the deck.

Ellie, then Paul, and finally Bob climbed the ladder and stood next to William.

"Now look up," William commanded, spreading his arms and aiming them skyward.

They all looked up to see a canopy of stars. In absolute wonderment, Paul looked up and said, "The sky is solid stars. It's like they are almost touching. It's almost like we can touch them. They're so big and bright."

"Big Sky Country with no city lights," said Bob. "If you look at them through binoculars, it's really spectacular. We may even be able to see the Milky Way."

"Well, I don't know if we're in 1805 Montana, but we're somewhere," said William. "I've got us set at fifteen feet and think we ought to stay there 'til morning. No need to turn on any lights unnecessarily, and I would rather not land in the dark."

Bob wrapped his big arm around Ellie's shoulders. "How does the 1805 Montana air smell?"

"It smells clean and fresh."

The crew sat in a semicircle around the Timer's upper deck, leaned back against the railing, and stared up at the sky.

Hugging her knees, Ellie said, "You know, I think we're going to get used to going to bed early."

"And not watching television," replied William.

"And getting up early," said Paul.

"And eating our own cooking," added Bob, slightly grimacing.

Then the four friends slipped on fleece jackets and settled down for the night. There wasn't much talking, but none of them got much sleep either. They were too excited.

CHAPTER 9

1805

THE SUN HAD not cleared the horizon when the friends were already up and eating breakfast. They had lowered the Timer to the ground and built a small fire. William and Bob had walked up to the river with two collapsible buckets and filled them with water. Each had a bowl of "mush," as Bob called it. William and Paul had fixed hot oatmeal with powdered milk and dried apples.

Ellie held her bowl near her mouth and blew on the hot mixture. "I'm almost too excited to eat."

Bob, amazed, looked at her. "Not me. I'll be happy to finish anything you excited people can't eat. This looks like something you would feed dogs and cats, but it's not bad. William, you and Paul should handle all the cooking."

"I think we'll let everyone share that duty though I would rather cook than clean up."

Looking thoughtful, William addressed the others. "I was thinking about something while Bob and I got the water. We didn't take bear spray with us. That probably wasn't the smartest thing we've ever done. There may be grizzlies around, and they aren't going to be afraid of us, so we'd better be afraid of them. Let's all remember that when we're away from the group, we should have our bear spray with us."

They all agreed.

The sky gradually brightened, and soon the sun's sharp edge peaked over the horizon. The sky rapidly took on a lustrous glow, and they took in their surroundings. As the sun rose, the shadows cast by trees changed from diffused to well-defined as if painted on the ground. They knew they were several hundred yards south of a river that made a bend to the north directly in front of them. Trees lined the river and followed its circuitous path across the plains. Tall, golden brown prairie grass waved in the breeze and covered rolling hills. This scene extended out of sight in all directions, with no sign of another living thing save a few circling birds.

"Before we leave, we need to plant a couple of homing beacons to get us back to this spot," said William. He carried two sixteen-inch steel cylinders down the ladder.

Ellie walked over and examined one of them. "Why do we need to come back to this spot?"

"The Timer sends and receives from roughly the same location. You don't have to be in the exact same place, but you need to be within fifty yards or so."

William dug two holes and buried the cylinders, leaving only inch-long square rods projecting above the ground. He carefully smoothed the earth and placed dry grass over the rods. A person would really have to look carefully to see them.

After disguising the two rods, they decided to walk to the river. William insisted they unpack several cans of bear spray and two of the dart pistols. When they reached the river, they took off their boots and waded in the water for a few minutes. Then they sat in the shade and let their feet dry. Paul and Bob assumed their favorite position—lying flat on their backs, staring up at the clouds.

Putting his socks and boots back on, William said, "Okay, let's straighten up camp, get packed, and head west." The friends soon walked back toward the Timer.

After washing the dishes, Bob said, "Let's get going. Paul, why don't you drive? I think you can handle the Timer with no problem. The more you drive, the more comfortable you'll be. You have enough practice time under your belt that William and I aren't worried in the least."

Rubbing his hands together, Paul looked at William. "Are you sure?"

"You know the steps. Crank her up and let's go."

William took a small, black compass from his pocket, flipped open the top, and studied the face for a minute. "I think that's got to be the Musselshell River, but regardless, it's headed in the right direction. North."

They climbed the ladder, and Paul settled behind the yoke in the driver's seat. He reached forward, flipped some switches, and began the warm-up procedure. The others took their positions, binoculars around their necks. William sat on the deck in front of Paul and scanned their intended path.

"Wow, where did these come from?" exclaimed Ellie as she waved her arms around her head.

The others started slapping at swarms of mosquitos that had suddenly appeared and seemed intent on finding exposed patches of skin. Clouds of them appeared where only a few moments before there had been none. The three lookouts scrambled below deck as Paul shut down the Timer. He clambered down behind them and pulled the hatch shut. They continued slapping and swatting until most of their tormentors were gone.

Ellie looked at the others. "I knew mosquitos could be bad in parts of the West, but this is ridiculous!"

Bob examined his itchy bites. "I've seen them worse. Get out the insect repellent."

They sprayed it on their hands, then transferred it to their faces, necks, wrists, and ankles. William and Ellie both pulled on caps, so now everyone had a covered head.

Ellie smeared the spray on the backs of her hands. "I hope this stuff works. I felt like I was getting eaten alive."

William laughed. "Once we get going, we should be okay. When we stop again, we may be glad we put it on."

They cautiously opened the hatch and climbed the ladder, quickly taking their seats. Paul pushed the stick forward, steered the Timer up, and then moved it out over the river, heading due north.

The mosquitos vanished almost as quickly as they appeared. With no pests to battle, the crew resumed scanning the horizon with their binoculars as the Timer moved with a low hum. It was almost as if the crew felt the sound instead of hearing it. It felt as if they were gliding through the air rather than hovering like a helicopter.

"Do you think we should travel at night?" Bob asked William.

"No, but I think there is something we need to do before we go any farther. Paul, drop us down near that small group of trees on the right."

Paul steered to the trees and lowered the Timer to the ground as delicately as if it were a falling leaf. William climbed down the ladder and walked over to some bushes, tore off some limbs, and tossed them up to the others on the deck. He repeated this several times and then called to the group.

"Hop down and help me. We are going to camouflage the Timer. Bob, get some of that line we stored."

Bob went down the hatch and returned with a coil of nylon line. He took out a steel pocketknife with a skeleton handle, flipped it open with one hand, and began cutting short lengths of cord. The others used the line to attach the leafy, green branches to the rail circling the top deck. Bob climbed down the ladder carrying an axe and used it to chop longer branches so they could hide the Timer's lower side. Soon the machine was festooned in greenery.

After a while William stopped, put his hands on his hips, and surveyed their work.

"It's going to look kind of like a floating haystack."

"I think it's going to look like someone has constructed a duck blind," suggested Bob.

"If it's harder to see, I don't care what it looks like," added Paul as he hung one last branch to the side of the Timer.

"One thing's for sure, it's a whole lot harder to tell what it is," said Ellie, laughing.

William started back up the ladder. "I'm satisfied. I think now we can fly or park next to trees and be harder to see."

They stored their gear, loaded back up, and Paul started them moving again. A little later, Bob disappeared below. In a few minutes, he returned with four thick ham-and-cheese sandwiches. Keeping one, he handed the others to his friends.

"I made some sandwiches before we left. We better eat them now. They won't be good for much longer. I doubt we'll run into a deli anywhere around here. I hope everyone likes spicy mustard."

The sandwiches were excellent, and they applauded Bob's thoughtfulness.

Paul kept the craft fifty yards to the left of the trees that skirted the river. Progress was slow, but at a steady fifteen miles per hour, they would cover a good distance before they stopped at dark. The river ran high and muddy, boiling over uprooted trees and tangles of brush that littered the bank like trash.

Suddenly, Ellie shouted, "Look up ahead!"

All eyes turned to an opening in the trees lining the banks to see a dozen or so American bison easing down to the river's edge to drink. They varied from huge, shaggy bulls to young calves. They walked belly deep in the water and crowded into one another. The adults made deep, bellowing sounds while the calves made high, bleating noises.

Paul stopped the Timer, and they all looked on, fascinated. As each great beast drank its fill, they slowly turned and climbed back up the bank with measured dignity then meandered up the hill bordering the river. As the last ones left, Paul pushed the stick forward, and they started up again.

They had followed the river for two hours when William exclaimed, "Missouri dead ahead! I believe. I hope."

At almost the same time, both Ellie and Bob spotted the great river leading off to the east. The water's surface was shiny silver, almost oily, as the slanting sunlight hit it at a perfect angle. Paul drove the Timer straight out over the wide river then made a slight turn to the left. Off to the west, they could see another river joining the Missouri. William said this was the Sacagawea River.

They moved steadily for several hours, watching a vast landscape of undulating grass roll by. It stretched out open and empty as far as they could see.

A ripping sound suddenly broke the silence; Bob had opened a candy bar, and, of course, everyone asked where it came from. Bob said he had a small supply and would share. He then finished the candy bar, licked his fingers, and put the wrapper back in his pocket. Picking up his binoculars, he resumed scanning. A few minutes later, he stopped and rubbed his eyes.

"I think I see something."

"What?" asked William.

Bob pointed to the west. Staring through his binoculars in that direction, William could see tiny dots moving up and away across a low hill. He lowered his binoculars.

"Impossible to say at this distance, but it might be Indians. Paul, continue west and steer as close as you can to the south bank. If someone looks our way, maybe we'll fade into the trees. I think that is one reason Dad used this dull gray color for the Timer."

"How far do we have to go before we get to the Great Falls of the Missouri?" Bob asked his brother as he shielded his eyes from the sun with his right palm. He had turned his cap backward because it interfered with his binoculars.

"It's really hard to say. As the crow flies, it's not that far. It's maybe two hundred miles following the river. The twists and turns add up. We could cut cross-country, but if we miscalculate, we might end up in Canada."

Bringing his binoculars back against his eyes, Bob replied, "I would really rather not go to Canada this trip."

Following instructions, Paul drove the Timer close to the south bank. At times, the trees screened them, but other times it was open plains. Whenever the trees and bushes dropped away, he lowered the Timer to less than ten feet. Paul said this gave the impression of skimming like a stone over the water's surface.

William was amazed at how easy it all appeared to be for Paul. "Paul, you should have been driving the whole time. You are already better than I ever was. "

The river rolled under the Timer and extended as far as they could see to the western horizon. Occasionally, they spotted buffalo herds looking like dark spots on the immense plains. Flying at this height and speed, through this tranquil setting, was a wonderful way to see the west.

"Look at those flowers!" Ellie suddenly yelled, pointing to a meadow beside the river.

Paul spun the Timer and drove it up and over the southern bank.

"Roses, I think," replied William as they cruised over them.

They were, indeed, wild red roses. Millions of them. They carpeted the ground like a bright red rug, a shock of color in an otherwise tan, brown, and green landscape. Ellie wanted to stop and pick some. The others discouraged this by telling her the mosquitos might return because the area was a little marshy. Even though Ellie wasn't sure she bought this, they pulled out over the Missouri and continued without stopping.

They resumed traveling and did so well into the evening. Nobody wanted to stop. It was a grand thing to travel across the huge, open, and empty country, with no planes, towns, roads, cars, or trains breaking the silence. The only sounds were their own voices and the Timer's gentle hum.

William rose from his seat on the deck, swept his arm toward the western horizon, and said, "I love this and hope you do too."

They all readily agreed. They loved the outdoors, and this was the ultimate outdoor adventure.

They traveled the rest of the afternoon without incident. As the shadows became longer, they looked for a place to spend the night and finally spotted one at a slight bend in the river. It would afford trees on three sides. Bob saw an opening leading from the river into the forest, and Paul crowded them through it. It was going to be a tight fit, but since they had decided to eat and sleep on the Timer for the time being, there was room enough. There was a small, open space for a fire, and that should be all they needed. Sleeping on the Timer suited William just fine because he was conscious of the fact that they were likely moving into conspicuous bear country. There was a great possibility they would run into one or more of the giant predators. He had read many stories of great grizzly bears in the early days of western exploration and had much respect for them. He said

Lewis and Clark knew nothing about them, but they learned fast. They were large, aggressive, and difficult to kill.

William looked at the surrounding trees. "Be sure you're armed."

Glancing at the trees, Bob turned to Paul. "Let's go catch some fish. I don't want to eat something out of a can or package tonight if I can help it. "

They retrieved fly rods and dart guns from storage and started toward the bank. Soon, they were casting away and shortly catching fish. They returned after an hour, bragging about not wanting to catch more than they could eat.

"Fat chance the two of you would catch more than you could eat," replied Ellie with a good-natured grin.

"We even cleaned them for you slackers," Bob said as he held them for inspection.

William and Ellie piled up some dry wood between the Timer and the trees, breaking off some of the small, brittle limbs and starting a fire. They got out a frying pan, salt, pepper, flour, and a little cooking oil.

"We need to go easy with the oil because there isn't much. Later, we can reduce some animal fat, but that probably isn't half as good," said William as he began blending the salt, pepper, and flour in a small bowl.

"It doesn't sound half as good," agreed Ellie, sticking out her tongue.

Looking at his brother, William asked, "Bob, did you and Paul clean those fish by the river and away from here? This cooking smell will probably attract every bear within twenty miles as it is."

"Yes, then threw the innards in the river."

Soon, William had dredged the fish, and they bubbled in the hot oil. William was right about the possibility that the smell might attract bears.

"That smells heavenly!" said Ellie, poking at the fish with the metal spatula she found in the Timer's kitchen supplies.

Soon the fish were browned on both sides, and she was dishing out the delicious treat to cries of acclaim. This meal was decidedly not out of a can.

William had found some flat pieces of driftwood that worked well as plates. "We can burn them when we finish rather than washing."

"Ellie, I think you're the best redheaded cook in Montana!" said Paul as he popped a piece of trout into his mouth.

"I'm probably the *only* redheaded cook in Montana," she quickly responded.

They finished the fish and dropped the remains in the river. Then they cleaned their frying pan and utensils by scrubbing them with good Montana dirt and rinsing them in the river. The crew gathered around the fire, sighing contentedly and discussing their day. Bob and Paul lay on the ground, their feet at the fire and their heads propped on a log they had drug over.

"I think we had a good first day," William said as he looked around the group.

"The best!" added Bob.

There were no mosquitoes, so they pulled sleeping bags through the hatch and decided to spend the night on the upper deck. This would be the first of many nights spent under the stars. There was a cool, steady breeze out of the west, and they thought this was probably why there were no mosquitoes. Bob said that because they were now almost exclusively over moving water, the mosquitoes would not be as bad. They rolled out their sleeping bags and spread them on the deck on top of self-inflating pads. Lying there looking up at the stars was just as they had experienced on the first night. It was as if you could reach out and touch them. Out came their binoculars.

"I thought you could see lots of stars with your eyes. This is like gazing at never-ending layers of stars," Paul said, wonderment in his voice.

Finally, one by one, sleep overwhelmed them and all was quiet.

The next morning, they had cold mush for breakfast. Bob said it made him yearn for the days of hot mush. "Eating this is going to make me waste away to nothing."

"Yep, that's right. You might waste away to less than two hundred and ninety pounds," retorted his brother with a grin.

After everyone took their sleeping gear below, Paul raised them off the ground and out over the Missouri. They followed the river for hours through an unchanging panorama of prairie and rolling hills. It was just afternoon when the river began a huge bend to the south.

William said they would soon be past the future location of Fort Benton. "The American Fur Company sold Fort Benton to the Army in 1865. It was on the trail to the goldfields in southern Montana like the famous Alder Gulch. Most of the goods that came by water ended up at Fort Benton. It was a thriving city and is still there today."

"As with most things, William knows more about it than I do, but I think at one time, Fort Benton was the port farthest inland in the world," Bob said.

"Bob's right, and a road led from Fort Benton to the Northwest that thousands of settlers took to the Washington-Oregon territory."

"The next landmark we'll see should be the Great Falls of the Missouri. William and I love waterfalls, so we're looking forward to that," Bob said with great anticipation.

"Is anyone else amazed we haven't met any Indians? This is Montana after all," stated Paul, looking at the brothers.

Carefully walking across the deck and seating himself in the chair next to Paul, William began to explain. "There are several things you have to remember. One, Montana is big, wide-open place! It's the fourth largest state and over one hundred and forty-five thousand square miles. We spend nine months of the year in New Hampshire. You could fit sixteen New Hampshire into Montana. Two, the population of Montana is forty-eighth out of the fifty states even in the twenty-first century. Right now, there are only six or seven Indian tribes scattered over all that area. It amounts to few people and lots of land."

"Wow, after hearing that, I'll be surprised to see any on this trip," said Paul as he stretched his arms and leaned back in his chair.

"I bet we see plenty before this trip is over. We are headed toward some of the population centers," added Bob.

After another hour, they rounded a bend in the river and William pointed ahead. "Look at that."

In the distance, the crew could see white-capped mountains peeking up from the plains and stretching north and south as far as they could see.

"Those are the Rocky Mountains!"

"Look at that!" said Paul as he reached for his binoculars.

"How will we get through that?" Ellie asked, with trepidation.

"There's a way," replied William. "If Lewis and Clark could get through, I know we can. We'll go around them as much as through them. Lewis and Clark had to go through them to get to the west coast. We're not going to the west coast."

"Not this time," said Bob with a wry smile.

Another hour passed. Ellie suddenly stood and pointed up the river. "William, is that a fire?"

In the distance, they could see what appeared to be smoke rising above the prairie.

"You think it might be a prairie fire, William?" asked Paul.

"I think it might be mist from the first of the falls," William said as he peered west, shading his eyes with his right hand.

CHAPTER 10

THE GREAT FALLS
AND THE RIVER

As THEY GOT closer to Ellie's fire, they heard a distant roar. It sounded like continuous thunder. What they thought was smoke was a heavy mist rising above the river like a damp, white blanket. As they rounded a bend, a huge waterfall stretched across the river up ahead.

"It must be sixty or seventy feet high!" said Bob.

"Actually, it's closer to eighty feet," replied William, who had to shout so they could hear him.

"Wow, it's hundreds of yards wide!" said Paul, astonishment on his face.

"It's just beautiful," added Ellie admiringly.

Paul drove the Timer closer to the southern end of the falls, where he was able to get to an angle so that they could see across its width. Bob quickly retrieved a camera from below and began taking pictures. William pointed out there would be no photos of the Great Falls at this age anywhere in the world.

"Pull over to the bank, Paul. I want to climb that hill and see what's ahead."

And with that, William climbed partway down the exterior ladder. Paul maneuvered the Timer against the bank, and William hopped off. He climbed the steep bank quickly, and at the top a stunning sight rewarded him. The rapids rolled away upriver, their magnitude unimaginable. You had to wonder if Lewis and Clark's hearts sank when they faced this view. William spotted more falls in the distance. After a few minutes, he went back to the river, and Paul swung the Timer over to pick him up. Bob reached down, grabbed his brother's hand, and practically lifted him to the upper deck.

"Meriwether Lewis said he saw some Indian lodges in that small wood over there, but I didn't see them," William said.

Paul turned to the brothers. "Well, what do we do now, and how do we get past these falls?"

William grinned. "We do like Lewis and Clark. We go around them."

Paul shook his head. "How did they get those heavy keelboats around the falls and through all this rough country?"

"They portaged the boats for miles. They pulled and pushed them up and down ravines and through briars, and they kept going until they were past the white water and falls. They made four trips. It was quite a feat."

"How far to the end of the falls, William?" Bob asked.

"About twelve miles."

"Wow! That's a long way to carry a canoe, much less a heavy wooden boat."

"Bob, I believe you have a newfound respect for the Corps of Discovery. They made wheels from the trucks of trees, but the wood was soft and continually breaking. It was some accomplishment."

"You said it!"

Following William's instructions, Paul steered downriver a few hundred yards and drove up and over a bank with a gentle slope that led to higher ground. As they reached the top of the hill, they were stunned as the Great Fall's true scope came into focus. The Missouri was a riot of white water and falls extending mile after mile into the distance. It was spectacular!

As they flew over the land bordering the river, the sounds of the falls and the white water crashing were deafening. The friends had to shout to one another. After passing each waterfall, Paul steered the Timer back out over the rapids and white water. It was exhilarating to cruise so low over the boiling, splashing tumult. The four friends had been white-water rafting many times and loved it; however, they had never done it like this. The carpet of water flowed beneath their feet. It was like surfing a white-water raft against the current. The spraying water rose so high they had to close the hatch. Soon they were all soaked, their clothes plastered to their skin like wetsuits.

After the third falls, Bob pointed to the bank nearest them and said, "Check that out."

They looked down to see a huge grizzly bear—a silvertip with a glossy coat and long, curving claws—on his hind legs, staring up at them. He roared at them, then dropped down on all fours and followed them for several hundred yards, occasionally standing on his rear legs and waving his talons at them.

"I'll stay far away from that monster," said Bob, awe in his voice.

William looked on in amusement. "Bob, remember, we're doing the trespassing, not him."

"You're right, and I'm still going to stay far away from him."

The Timer continued following the river, circling around the falls and flying low over the rapids. Bob said he had never been wet and dry in the same day so much in his life. They would get wet over the rapids and partially dry out going around the falls.

They were flying along after the fourth falls when William shaded his eyes and called to Paul. "See where that water is flowing into the river over there on the east bank? Let's go take a closer look."

Paul drove the Timer toward the bank where water rushed down a cascade of rock and into the river.

"Bob, do you recognize that?" he asked his brother.

"Is it Giant Springs?"

"That's exactly what it is."

Laughing, Ellie spoke up, "Okay, I'll bite. What is Giant Springs?"

Turning to Ellie, William pointed at the bank. "Actually, what you're looking at is the shortest river in the world. That's the Roe River, and it's two hundred feet long. It's being fed by Giant Springs, which you're about to see next."

As the Timer cleared the top of the bank, they saw an expanse of water covered with ducks and geese, and they swam immediately to the far side of the pond.

William switched to his professorial voice. "Giant Springs is well-named. The water you see comes from the Little Belt Mountains, fifty or sixty miles away. Pressure forces it to the surface here from four hundred feet down. Want to take a guess how much water flows out each day?"

"How about a hundred thousand gallons?" Ellie guessed.

Wagging his right index finger, William replied, "One hundred and fifty million gallons."

"One hundred and fifty million a day? You have got to be kidding!"

"Nope, I'm not, pretty amazing, huh? Okay, Paul, let's get going."

There were five falls along the Missouri, different heights and shapes, but all special. It was a wonderful afternoon under sunny skies and cool breezes with awesome sights and sounds. Everyone felt great, but that was about to change.

They cruised along the south bank at the usual fifteen feet and fifteen miles per hour. Time passed, and they approached a small, wooded island just beyond the last of the rapids.

Bob leaned over to Paul. "Drop down on that island and let's catch some fish. The breakfast mush has worn off, and I'm starving."

Paul set the Timer down in a clearing next to the bank. He and Bob retrieved their fishing gear from below deck, tied their favorite flies to their lines, and climbed down the ladder. For a minute, they debated which side of the island to fish and finally decided to fish the side where the current swept between the island and the closest river-bank. With William and Ellie cheering them on, they began catching fish, and soon each had several flopping on the bank near their feet. They were excited and focused on dropping their flies upstream and letting them float down to a hole and the waiting fish. This section of the river had obviously never been fished; the fish were eager to bite.

Suddenly, Ellie shouted, "Paul! Bob! Watch out! Here come some bears!"

William's eyes followed Ellie's finger and rested on five grizzly bears emerging from some trees less than seventy-five yards away. They spun around and ran toward the Timer. The bears roared and charged. William jumped in the driver's seat as Paul and Bob sprinted.

Paul, a few yards ahead of Bob, leaped for the ladder. His right foot landed on the ladder's second rung, and he began to scramble up. At the same time, Bob's right foot slipped on one of the freshly caught fish, causing him to fall and slide toward the bank. He seemed to have no chance of getting high enough on the ladder to get out of the bears' reach as they closed in quickly.

William, fear in his face, yelled for Bob to get in the river. As Paul's head appeared coming up the ladder, William quickly turned and said, "Hold on, we've got to get this thing moving."

Bob was up in a flash and dove into the river. A large male continued in Paul's direction while two other bears followed Bob to the spot on the riverbank where he had gone into the water.

The Timer came to life as Paul's bear swiped at his foot. The big paw hit his boot heel and knocked his foot off the rung. Paul swung free for a second, but he held the ladder tightly. He lifted his feet as high as he could, placing them on a higher rung. Grabbing the railing, he vaulted up, and as he clambered onto the Timer's deck, he still clutched his fly rod in his left hand. There were four deep gouges in the lower side of his right boot.

Meanwhile, Bob swam away from the bank as another bear splashed into the water after him. Bob was a strong swimmer, but his boots and clothes slowed him down considerably. He had a head start, but the bear rapidly closed in.

The Timer heeled over as William swung it around and dropped it toward his struggling brother. Paul fell and skidded across the deck on his back. However, he was able to catch the rail and stop himself from going over the side.

"Yell at the bear!" William ordered the others as he lowered the Timer close to the water's surface. Paul and Ellie immediately began shouting at the bear and waving to get his attention.

It worked! The bear slowed for a second, looked back over his shoulder and then up at Paul and Ellie. This was all the time Bob needed to quickly increase his lead from five to ten feet as William dropped the ladder next to him.

"Grab on! I'll pull you away from him and then you can climb on."

Bob gripped the lowest rung, and William drove upriver and away from the bear. When they were fifty yards ahead, William stopped the Timer and the others helped an exhausted Bob aboard.

"I was afraid to try to lift you clear of the water. I didn't know if you were too tired to hold on."

Bob looked at William.

"Good call, bro. I'm not sure I could have held on. I would have hated to have fallen on my friend down there." He pointed back at the bear still swimming toward them.

William moved the stick and swung the Timer around. They cruised back over the scene of excitement, where they saw six bears enjoying the boys' catch.

Bob looked down at the bears then turned to Paul. "Do you have a treble hook?"

"I think so."

He looked through his tackle box, handed Bob a three-pronged hook. Bob took Paul's rod and placed the treble on the leader.

Bob turned to William. "Move left about fifteen feet and drop down a little." Bob leaned over the railing.

"Bob, be careful!" William admonished. "I think the last thing you want to do is drop on the heads of a group of hungry bears."

"I want my fly rod back," retorted Bob. He leaned over the railing and after several tries managed to snag his rod and reel it in.

"I don't believe that one will be too hard to clean," snickered Paul.

William, relieved, lifted the Timer back to fifteen feet and said, "Lewis and Clark mentioned an island and named it White Bear Island because it had so many bears. I wonder if this is it?"

"The name sure fits," said Bob ruefully.

William turned the Timer back over to Paul and said, "Let's find a place to spend the night, away from these bears."

Bob pointed back down the river. "I say we spend the night near that last set of falls. There was a meadow by the river's edge, surrounded by trees on three sides. It should be a good spot to catch supper...again."

Paul laughed and drove back down the river to Bob's meadow. He eased the Timer through a narrow opening in the trees, pushing aside the top of one young one. Red, blue, purple, and yellow flowers covered the ground. The riverbank was right at the falls' edge, and a light mist rose from the bottom, coating the closer trees in glossy moisture. Ellie said this was probably the reason for the profusion of flowers. This would be especially true when the wind blew across the river. Most of the moisture would come right into the meadow.

Bob stood up and patted his stomach. "I want some fresh trout for supper."

William looked at him, "Do you need some help? I'm beat."

"Nope, all of you rest. I'll catch plenty."

He gathered his rod, tackle box, and rifle and started east along the riverbank.

"You're not going to fish where we can watch?" asked William.

"No, I'm going to fish a spot we passed on the way upriver. There was a quiet eddy near the bank which is going to hold fish. I'm also going to carry a long gun, just in case."

Bob walked back for about a half mile and sat down on a suspended log to rig his hook. He opened his tackle box and sifted through several flies before selecting one, a popping bug that would surely look tasty to a trout. He attached it, closed his tackle box, and started to get up and move down to the bank. Suddenly, out of the corner of his eye, he noticed movement. He slowly turned his head and saw a man coming out of the brush and rapidly walking in his direction!

Bob eased his back to the ground and turned onto his stomach. He then swung his feet and legs around. He flattened himself as much as possible and from beneath the log watched a man in buckskin walking by at a fast pace. Lean, muscular, and very tan, the guy's hair receded above his temples, hanging long down his back. He seemed intent on getting closer to a small buffalo herd headed to the bank to drink. Bending at the waist, he crept behind a tree that had fallen into the river and washed up on the bank. The buffalo were on the same side of the river, about a hundred yards away.

As Bob watched, the stranger propped his rifle on the tree trunk and sighted down the long barrel. He took his time, obviously wanting to make his shot count. Abruptly, he fired. When the rifle discharged with a loud bang, Bob jumped and banged his head on the log. The gun's butt slammed powerfully back against the man's shoulder. Blue smoke formed a cloud and rose around the shooter. A buffalo staggered, fell to its knees, and rolled over on his side. The other buffalo spun around and galloped away across the plains. The hunter yelped for joy, sprang up, and started toward the fallen, still animal.

Bob rubbed the top of his head and watched breathlessly as this drama played out in front of him. He wanted to congratulate the man on the excellent shot but finally decided that might not be a good idea. He needed to discuss this with his crew members before making contact with other people.

The hunter had gone only a few yards when he turned to look back over his shoulder for the source of a frightening roar. A huge grizzly bear reared up, crashed through the low bushes, and started running toward the hunter. The man whirled completely around, raised his gun, and made ready to fire. Then he dropped the rifle to his side. He had forgotten to reload.

He turned and started running away from the bear at top speed. The grizzly dropped to all fours and leaped after him. Bob could tell the man was fast but could also tell he wasn't nearly fast enough. The bear gained on him rapidly.

Bob stayed low as the man ran past. Then he realized that the bear would go by thirty feet from him. By this time, the man had run toward the riverbank and made a flying leap as far out into the water as his momentum would carry him. He landed in chest-deep water, holding his rifle with both hands high above his head.

His charging, roaring, fearsome adversary closed in quickly. As the bear bounded past, Bob raised his gun and snapped off a shot, firing a dart into the bear's left hip. Bob knew that just one dart would not stop the bear in time, but he hoped it would distract him.

Then a miracle occurred. The bear slid to a stop at the water's edge. He turned his great head and bit at the dart in his hip then turned back and looked at the man standing in the water. Now clutching his rifle by the barrel, the man obviously intended to use it as a club in what would have surely been a futile attempt at self-defense. The bear shook its head and with a low growl turned and retreated, going back in the direction from which he had come.

Bob stayed low and hoped the hunter couldn't spot him over the bank's edge. He inched back several feet, keeping his head down as he waited for him to come ashore. He heard scrambling noises, then muttering, and then a strange flapping sound. Bob had to see what it was. He peeked over the log and saw the man facing the river, waving, and shaking the water out of his buckskin coat.

Bob dropped back behind the log and, in a minute, heard the man walk away. He peeked up one more time and saw him walk toward the buffalo he shot then stop twenty yards from it and sit on a log. He pulled around a bag that was slung over his shoulder and loaded his gun. He'd learned his lesson about carrying an unloaded weapon in dangerous territory. After loading, he stood and walked over to the fallen animal. Taking the gun in one hand, he used it to poke the buffalo's eye. No movement. It was dead.

"Okay, let's get out of here while the getting is good," Bob whispered to himself.

He turned and crawled into some low sage bushes and then duck-walked low to the ground until he reached the closest stand of trees. He stood up and, reached behind himself, placed his palms on his lower back, stretching. He draped his gun over his right shoulder and headed back to camp.

When Bob walked in, Paul fired the first question. "Where are the fish?"

Bob, with a tired smile, told the story of the hunter and the bear. "I'm really glad neither one saw me."

William grinned and snapped his fingers. "You know what you just did?"

"No."

"You just saved Meriwether Lewis."

"Huh?"

"You just saved Meriwether Lewis. There is a story of a grizzly bear chasing Meriwether Lewis to the river and for some reason not jumping in after him. He never had a good explanation for what saved him. Now we know."

"You have to be kidding!"

"I'm not. He could never understand why the bear suddenly stopped, turned, and didn't follow him into the river. He was very happy about it but never understood it."

They sat around, pondering how differently things might have turned out. What would have become of the Corps of Discovery if the bear had killed Meriwether Lewis? The men would have probably reached the west coast and returned, but the great expedition would have changed in ways unknown. William said that the lack of Lewis's journal alone would have been a major loss.

"Imagine if we didn't have all of his sketches and notes. Imagine the samples that would not have been taken and brought back to President Jefferson. The expedition would not have failed, but its impact would have lessened."

"I wonder if we could sneak over and see what they're doing," Bob said. "We could stand at the edge of the trees and see if they came back to clean the buffalo he shot."

"Let's try," agreed Paul.

"I'm game," Ellie joined in.

"Let's be careful, very careful," added William.

The friends followed Bob back through the trees. In a few minutes, they were crawling to the edge of the woods. Staying low, they looked around trees and through sagebrush at a group of men gathered around the dead buffalo. They were butchering the animal, laying the meat on the inside of a piece of the skin they removed. Other men walked back toward the east with great hunks of meat thrown over their shoulders.

"They seem pretty efficient at their work. I guess if our next meal depended on how well we did that, we would be pretty good too," said William, placing his elbows on the ground and propping his chin in his hands.

"Wonder if they'll leave any for us," Bob said. The others put their hands over their mouths to suppress laughter.

"I suspect they'll take all the best parts and leave the rest for scavengers," said William.

"Scavengers like me or like that bear I shot?"

"I think the bear. He might have to chase off some birds, but I bet he'll show back up. Bears have a great sense of smell."

"What in the world is that?" Ellie asked in a hoarse whisper, pointing to a man carrying a large, bloody, odd-looking piece of meat.

Bob buried his face in his hands and let out a choked laugh. "You don't know what that is?"

"No, I do not know what that horrible-looking thing is."

"That's a buffalo tongue. Believe it or not, it's one of the best parts of the buffalo. It was considered a delicacy."

"I would never eat that disgusting-looking thing!"

William rolled over on his right side to look at Ellie. "If you didn't know what it was and it was grilled, fried, or cooked in a stew, you would love it."

"Have you ever eaten any?"

"Yep, and it was pretty good."

"Nope, it was delicious!" Bob added.

"Yuck! I repeat, I would not eat any of those horrid-looking things."

As they looked on, the men finished loading up the meat on the buffalo skin and started back to their camp. They operated quickly and efficiently, with little wasted motion.

Slowly and stealthily, Ellie kneeled and removed a camera from her pocket. Extending the lens, she snapped photos as fast as the camera would work.

"Good girl, Ellie. You're smarter than the rest of us," whispered William, patting her back. "Think about it. Actual pictures of the Lewis and Clark Expedition in 1805 Montana."

"Imagine how much meat it takes to feed thirty men every day," said Bob, appearing to do the calculations in his head.

"What do they eat besides buffalo?" Paul asked.

William turned on his other side to face Paul. "That was pretty much it. They ate on average nine pounds a day."

"Nine pounds a day! You have got to be kidding!"

"What is so strange about that? Sounds about right to me," said Bob with a laugh.

Ellie stared at him, "Bob, even you don't eat that much meat."

William reached over and patted his brother's broad shoulder. "I say let's get out of here before the scavengers, including Bob's furry friend, show up."

They retraced their steps through the trees, returning to the Timer with no fish and no buffalo, which William and Paul quickly pointed out to Bob.

William then looked around at the others. "I really think we should move on down the river. I don't think we should get tangled up with Lewis and Clark and their men if we don't have to. Who knows how that might affect things? I think it would be a big mistake to have to explain ourselves to them."

"What about the clothes we washed while Bob was out saving Meriwether Lewis's life?" asked Ellie.

Ellie had talked Paul and William into helping her wash some of their laundry because she didn't know when they might get another chance. They had biodegradable soap and, with the river close at hand, washed the clothes in no time. Now there were wet clothes draped over bushes, logs, and limbs around their camp.

"Hang them on the railing," directed William. "When we start moving, they should dry out pretty quickly."

"Good idea," said Ellie.

The group decided to have a cold supper of oatmeal with some wild berries they had picked near the river. Bob complained about the meal because he had really wanted grilled fish.

"Too bad," said his brother in mock sympathy.

"These blueberries are really good," said Paul through a mouthful of oatmeal.

"Correction. In Montana, those are not blueberries. Those are the much better huckleberries."

"They look like blueberries."

"They are huckleberries in Montana," said Bob, emphatically shaking his head.

After they had cleaned up the area and hung the wet clothes on the railing, Paul took the pilot's seat, raised the Timer, and away they went. They cautiously pulled out over the river, saw no one, and resumed their trek to the west. The Missouri continued to provide the perfect trail, easy to follow, with no obstructions.

William cautioned everyone to keep their eyes peeled and their binoculars moving. The close run-in with Meriwether Lewis had made them all nervous. They were obviously not as far ahead of the expedition as they had thought. It was also true, though, that Meriwether Lewis was known to have taken long hikes far ahead of his party.

"He couldn't have been that far ahead, though, because some of the others came up pretty fast to get that buffalo meat," Bob pointed out.

CHAPTER 11

TRAVELING WEST

Paul hugged the river's south bank with the Timer. This made them less visible to both the Native American population and the Corps of Discovery. As long as there were no long gaps between the trees, they stood a good chance of remaining unseen. Paul had to make some tricky maneuvers in several places to dodge trees or other spots where the bank protruded into the water. All in all, it was not difficult driving, and they made good time. They flew for an hour and a half before William suggested they find a place to spend the night. It was getting late, and they had put close to twenty miles between themselves and Lewis and Clark. They intended to get an early start each day so there seemed little chance of them losing ground to the Corps.

Ellie spotted their new campground, a small clearing partially surrounded by rock piles. Paul squeezed the Timer past several trees and put it down between the rocks and the river on a flat area overlooking the Missouri's low bank.

After climbing down from the Timer, they settled into the rocks and started prepping a fire. William built a fire ring of softball-size rocks while Bob and Paul pushed over larger rocks for seats. Soon, sheltered in their alcove, they had a roaring fire, which they gathered around and discussed their day.

They were hungry, so they opened two large packages of freeze-dried lasagna and poured a pot of boiling water over it. William insisted all their drinking and cooking water be boiled thoroughly because there were so many animals present. He didn't want anyone getting giardia, especially in the middle of nowhere. Bob said this was the first real food he had had in days.

"I could have eaten that entire buffalo by myself."

After supper, they again considered whether they should be flying at night. For the time being, it was a matter of keeping a close eye out for Native Americans. So for now, they would continue to travel by day.

"We would miss too much if we spent the whole time traveling at night," Bob pointed out. And it was a valid reason...for now.

The friends chatted a few minutes more, and then their fire began making low, sputtering noises because of light rainfall. To be on the safe side, they extinguished it by kicking dirt over it.

The friends climbed the ladder to the deck and descended into the Timer's interior. Leaving the hatch slightly cracked so they could hear the rain, they crawled into their sleeping bags. They enjoyed sleeping outside most of the time, but it sure was cozy inside during bad weather. Bob said it was almost like sleeping in one of their homes in New Mexico that had a tin roof. He said it sounded like a person playing the same notes over and over on a xylophone. Also, the Timer circulated air from the outside and kept the inside at a comfortable temperature, preventing the interior from ever becoming stuffy.

Their talking gradually quieted, and they fell sound asleep. They never dreamed they would retire so early each night, but now it was routine, with the early rising and long summer days.

They woke the next morning to bluebird skies and a bright yellow sun rising. Rubbing their eyes, they climbed out onto the upper deck and watched until the entire sun had risen above the horizon and into the sky. Climbing down and making their way to the campsite, they used the remnants of the boiled water from the night before to make cold, instant oatmeal. This was now definitely not their favorite meal, but as Bob said, it did stick to your ribs. They scrubbed the dishes with dry grass until they glistened and stored them away. Then they loaded up on the upper deck and headed west. As usual, Paul kept the Timer low, clinging to the river's south bank.

The weather was cool and refreshing as a light breeze rippled the water's surface. Some wood ducks flew out of a small slough, with water droplets cascading behind them and making a rain pattern that followed them across the river. About that time, Bob screwed up his nose. "What is that smell?"

William looked at him. "Now that you mention it, whatever it is, it's very unpleasant."

"Unpleasant?" said Ellie. "It's horrid!"

They rounded a bend, and an unbelievable sight greeted them: dozens and dozens of dead buffalo stacked against the bank. They were twisted at all kinds of angles, some even appearing to be standing up. The current had apparently piled them up. The smell was almost overwhelming.

Bob scrambled below and returned with T-shirts that everyone tied over their noses. "I think my T-shirt smells worse than the buffalo."

Everyone laughed, and things lightened up.

"This is appalling. What could have caused it?" inquired Ellie.

William leaned his elbows on the railing and stared at the pile of dead animals. "They probably got caught by fast-rising, swift-running water while they tried to cross upriver. They floated down to this point, and the current piled them up in the bend."

"Makes sense," said Paul. "It still happens in our time."

William leaned back. "You know, the definition of 'our time' has changed a lot in the last few weeks."

Bob stood, intertwining his fingers across his broad brow to shade his eyes. "The smell doesn't seem to be bothering them too much."

The others looked across the river to see six large wolves trotting over a rise and then down toward the dead buffalo. The wolves ranged in color from light gray to almost black, and all looked healthy, big, and strong.

"I think they see a banquet," said Ellie. "It may be a smelly one to us, but I think it must smell great to them."

"Well, I think he sees one too," Paul said as he pointed out an enormous grizzly bear coming up to the south bank behind them.

He walked within fifty yards of the Timer, never taking his eyes off the large meal across the river. As they watched, the bear slid down the bank into the water and started swimming across.

William turned to Paul. "Get us out of here. I've had enough of this stench. I doubt the view will improve now that the eating is about to begin."

All agreed with this splendid idea. None of them had a weak stomach, but they had a good idea what was about to happen and didn't want to witness it.

Spitting over the side, Bob pinched his nose and said, "I do believe I can actually taste that smell."

CHAPTER 12

SIGHTS ALONG
THE MISSOURI

PAUL PUSHED THE lever forward, and the Timer moved away at its usual fifteen feet above the river. Much to the crew's delight, they soon put the river bend's sight and smell behind them.

As they cruised down the river, Paul asked, "What is the next interesting thing to see?"

"Uh, Paul, did you think that last scene was interesting?" asked Bob as he tried to pinch Paul's nose.

William looked around. "I haven't spent that much time this far down the Missouri, but I think we should be getting close to the White Cliffs."

With a quizzical look, Ellie asked, "What are the White Cliffs? Do you think we'll round the next bend and be in England?"

William smiled. "You'll see."

"What William is trying to say, Ellie, is that you can't explain them to someone. You have to see them for yourself," added Bob.

"Oh! Then they should be, as Paul would say, interesting."

As they continued up the river, the wildlife amazed them: hundreds of ducks, geese, and pelicans on the water and in the air, as well as the occasional eagle, both golden and bald. Twice they saw eagles swoop down to the river and snatch up fish and also spotted deer and elk along the riverbank. Surprisingly, they saw few buffalo.

About that time Ellie shouted, "Look at the beaver!"

They looked farther up the river and could see two beavers making their way across to the north bank.

"What's a beaver doing here? There's not a tree in sight," Paul asked, mystified.

"Those beaver aren't dam builders," responded Bob. "They can live out here in the big river."

"I never knew that type of beaver existed," replied Paul.

After traveling several more hours, the banks began to steepen. Soon they were milky white and soaring hundreds of feet into the air, almost completely vertical and forming many fantastical and bizarre shapes.

"Those look like Roman ruins," said Ellie. "Look at the columns, walls, and parapets."

Pointing farther up the river, she said, "There are some that look like an old fortress."

"That one looks like a church steeple!" added Bob.

"I've never seen anything like this," said Paul. "It's probably the most incredible thing I have ever seen! How far do they run, William?"

"Hard as it is to believe, they run for forty-six miles in one form or another."

"That *is* hard to believe. Forty-six miles!"

"That one looks like a set of bowling pins," responded Ellie. "Did you say forty-six miles?"

"Yep, forty-six miles, that is a four, followed by a six."

"Some of these cliffs must be three hundred feet high!" Ellie said, her voice full of awe. "Some of these walls look man-made. They're tall and only a couple of feet thick. It's pretty amazing that erosion formed them."

"It's amazing all right, but wait until you see some of the sights in Yellowstone," William replied. "They make some of this stuff look tame. You'll see why some of the earlier Yellowstone visitors were considered great frontiersmen and even greater liars."

Ellie took numerous photos as the White Cliffs and exotic formations continued. They agreed it would be interesting to compare pictures taken today with future photos of the White Cliffs.

William stretched his legs and crossed his ankles. "You know, it's almost overkill. There is so much, but we look at these formations along here and barely comment."

The Timer continued moving up the river, and it seemed the formation variations were endless. The crew knew they were getting to see something unique. Each river bend presented new sights. Herds of bighorn sheep stared at them from cliff tops. It seemed almost impossible that four-legged animals could stand on such precarious perches, walking on narrow footholds as if they had no worries. There were birds of every description; as William pointed out, some of them didn't make it to the twenty-first century.

Finally exiting the White Cliffs region, Paul cruised along the south bank at top speed. Time passed, and the river started narrowing. They entered a canyon with towering walls that rose hundreds of feet and cast the river into shadows. The air temperature dropped noticeably, and the water flow sped up considerably.

Bob leaned back, looked upward, and said, "This is what Lewis and Clark called the 'Gates of the Rocky Mountains.'"

Paul looked at the cliffs' sunless, black sides and the river's deep green water and said, "Boy, this is what I would call dismal! How would you like to pull a boat through this?"

In less than an hour, they left the gloomy canyon behind, and a wondrous sight greeted them: flower-covered mountain meadows as far as they could see and, behind them, snow-peaked mountains.

"It looks like an old movie's painted background," said Paul.

"Wow!" exclaimed Ellie. "What a beautiful country. "

"It is," William agreed. "Remember, this is where the Corps of Discovery began to meet Indians. We'd better be careful. Keep those binoculars moving, and let's watch for men, horses, and especially smoke."

"Why smoke?" asked Paul.

"Easy to see and usually means people."

CHAPTER 13

COMPANY

THE NEXT SEVERAL days were warm and the nights cool, with the now-familiar bluebird skies and occasional afternoon showers followed by sunshine. This made the water droplet on leaves and flowers shine like diamonds. The country was absolutely glorious with picture-postcard views everywhere. They continued to see birds of all description, buffalo, and sheep. They also saw more bears than they had seen in the last two weeks. They ate—and enjoyed—fat fish from the river. Fishing had become Bob and Paul's late afternoon ritual, and eating the fish for supper had become everyone's evening ritual. Ellie tried to think of different ways to prepare them other than frying and baking. They continued to drive the Timer close to the south bank, hoping to avoid detection. So far, it seemed to be working.

The second night after they passed the Gates of the Rocky Mountains, they pulled into a small meadow a short distance from the riverbank and set up camp. Paul and Bob took their fishing gear and dart guns to the water to catch their meal. They returned in a few minutes with cleaned fish, and soon Ellie had them sizzling and popping in a frying pan over a small fire.

After eating, they settled back on the Timer deck for some stargazing. This was now one of their favorite pastimes, at least when the mosquitoes were not too bad. They moved their sleeping bags to the top deck, and one by one, they began to fall asleep.

Finally, only William was awake, and he continued staring skyward through his night-vision scope. Millions of stars seemed to hover just above their heads. There were so many that familiar constellations like the Big Dipper were difficult to see because they faded into the mass. He never got tired of the sight.

As William lowered his nightscope, a shadow moved into view in the corner of his right eye...at least it seemed to be a shadow... and he turned his head toward it. Through the dense trees, he saw a shape that seemed to move out on the river's center. How could this be? Could it be a sail on a Corps of Discovery boat? Why would they travel at night?

William raised his nightscope and kept it trained on the object. There was a small opening on the riverside of their meadow, so whatever it was should soon move into view. In a few seconds, he had a completely unrestricted view of it: a black, cylindrical, metal craft of some sort.

He could distinguish lines of rivets walking up its sides, and it was shaped like an old submarine. About fifty feet long, it had a stubby conning tower in the center. A circle of light shone through a round window set on the conning tower's side. William could just make out what appeared to be a person's head and shoulders projecting through the tower's top. He could not tell if it was male or female but presumed it to be the vessel's pilot. He heard a faint humming noise coming from the mystery craft.

William thought about waking the others but decided against it. He was afraid they might make too much noise, either from being awakened or when seeing the strange ship. He sat quietly until it disappeared around a river bend.

William wondered what it might have been, and then he thought he knew the answer. There were no flying machines in 1805. There was no technology to match what he had just seen. One by one, he rejected possibilities until he was forced into the only one: it had to be other time travelers.

Now that the mystery timer had passed, he debated with himself about waking the others. Ultimately, he decided to let them sleep. What could they do or what could he tell them that could make a difference right now? What could he show them? What could they see? William folded his hands behind his head and lay back, staring at the sky. He thought about what he had just seen. He concluded that contact with this new ship would probably not be a good thing for them and was probably something they should avoid at all costs. He had a strange, bad feeling about it.

The next morning, William woke before dawn. He had barely slept, spending a good deal of the night trying to decide what to tell the others. It was a complicated situation. Did he tell them or keep it to himself? Finally, he decided, while not positive about what he had seen, he should tell them what he thought. Whether his presumption was right or not, they had the right to know about the potential danger. As he thought about it, he built a small fire, careful to use the driest wood to avoid making too much smoke. Then he made hot chocolate with a powdered mix, sugar, and powdered milk—a recipe that had already proven to be popular on these cool mornings.

The others woke up slowly, stretching and going to the river as a group, their chosen way to travel because of the earlier bear encounters.

After splashing water on their faces, they returned to William's fire and helped themselves to the hot chocolate. They held their mugs in both hands and blew across the tops to cool the drinks enough to enjoy. William suggested they alternate cocoa and coffee in order to make each last longer. After finishing their morning treat, everyone began spooning bubbling oatmeal into the same mugs as they had decided a little chocolate never hurts anything. Then the blowing, cooling process began again, and they finished their oatmeal in short order. Bob and Paul scraped the last of the breakfast out of the cooking pot.

After they washed the dishes and William cleaned the cooking pot, they gathered around the fire to warm themselves and chat about the upcoming day...or so they thought.

William let the small talk die down.

"Get a grip on yourselves while I tell you what I saw last night."

"Did I miss another meteor shower?" Paul asked. "That makes at least three."

"No, that's not what you missed. Presuming our calculations are correct and I don't believe they're off by more than a week or two, I think I saw the impossible last night."

"What do you think you saw, William?" asked Bob.

William leaned in close as if whispering. "I saw a flying machine that I think must have been another timer."

"Whoa! I don't know what I thought you were going to say, but I know that wasn't it. Another timer, for real?"

"Are you serious?" asked Ellie. "There was nothing flying around here in 1805."

"Well, we are," said William. "There was nothing much flying anywhere in 1805 and certainly not around here. Common sense says it couldn't have been another timer, but after sitting up half the night, that's the only explanation I can come up with."

Bob looked at his brother. "Maybe that was why Dad was such a stickler about security and protecting the Timer."

William steepled his fingertips. "Dad was definitely very security-conscious. Someone would have a really difficult time getting through the security measures at home. But out here? Well, that's another story. If I were going to attempt to steal the Timer from us, I would certainly try it out here first."

Bob poked at the fire with a stick. "I wonder if the guy who built the Timer with Dad possibly sold the plans to someone else."

"I don't think so. Dad prided himself in being able to read people's character. I certainly don't think he would have sold them for the money. You know how much money Dad paid him."

"I guess you're right. The plans could have been stolen or one of the other scientists who knew how it worked could have sold them."

William scratched his head. "There is another possibility."

"What?" asked Bob.

"His family if he had one. They may have been in touch with the bad guys on the other timer. Or the bad guys may have been in touch with them. I just have a feeling we better consider them bad guys until we know better. They may have forced the plans from him with a threat to harm his family," said William.

Looking thoughtful, Bob said, "Well, from what you said, their timer doesn't look like ours."

"That's right. I thought about that. But not all boats, planes, and cars look alike either, but most work about the same."

The friends discussed this strange turn of events, pondering what to do. Bob wondered again if they should travel at night, but as William pointed out, nighttime was when he saw them.

"I'm not sure that's a good idea. We could get close to them before we knew it. Both of us are kind of hard to see at night.

"Also, I think they have to sleep sometime. Surely, they don't travel twenty-four hours a day."

"Unless they work in shifts. Maybe they have night and a day crew. It's hard to figure," wondered Bob.

Sipping water from his mug, William mused, "Their crew probably isn't much bigger than ours, so I doubt they drive in shifts. Do you think they're trying to sneak up on us? I think that may be the case. Right now, I wouldn't doubt anything."

"I think you're right," Ellie proffered. "It's too much of a coincidence for them to be in the middle of 1805 Montana at the same time as we are."

"As small as we are and as big as this country is, we may be the proverbial needle in a haystack," said Bob.

William took charge and said, "Okay, here's what we're going to do. We will travel during the day but not right on the river. We can follow the land's contours, keeping the river occasionally in sight but not to the point that we're easily seen."

The others agreed this sounded like a good plan. They also decided they should refresh the Timer's camouflage as often as possible.

"We'll keep an eye on the river and the land in front of us. We don't want to fly into a trap," William added.

William, Bob, and Ellie got their binoculars and the spotting scope and arranged themselves on the Timer's top deck. Paul drove. Each spotter had a point on the compass: south, southwest, and due west.

Paul lifted the Timer, creeping slowly and cautiously out of the trees. He headed south, away from the river, for several hundred yards. Then, with the others' assistance, he chose a course that ran parallel to it, trying to fly lower than normal at about ten feet. Even flying at this height, following every depression and ravine that lay in their path, they could still see the river frequently enough to follow it. Paul did his best to make sure they were never silhouetted against the sky by going around hilltops instead of directly over them. This travel style was certainly not as fast as following the river directly, but it seemed much safer.

Because they flew so low, the others had to periodically warn Paul about trees, large bushes, and boulders that might present problems. Fortunately, much of the land was open, and they did not have to warn Paul too often. They traveled like this all morning before they pulled into a grove for lunch.

As she bit into a peanut-butter-and-jelly sandwich, Ellie asked Bob and William, "How much longer will we follow the Missouri? I think getting away from it means getting away from that other timer. That has to be a good thing."

"I'm really not sure, but I don't think it will be too much longer. Our maps don't help much. We're only about a hundred years ahead of the roads shown on them. It's kind of guesswork," answered Bob as he unfolded a map and showed her.

William leaned back against the railing. "We can follow either the Gallatin or the Madison River. Bob and I thought the Madison would be the better one. The Gallatin should be the first river we come to turning south. The Madison would be the second to the left. The Gallatin takes a more direct route to Yellowstone while the Madison goes farther west into Idaho or what will become Idaho."

Bob looked first at his brother then at the others. "If we take the Madison River and leave it as it starts due south, we can enter Yellowstone from the southwest corner. We can travel northeast and see more of the park."

"What's at the southwest corner?" inquired Paul.

"The southwest corner is called Cascade Corner. It has the largest concentration of waterfalls in the park, and they're beautiful. It's really a neat area," said Bob.

"It will be interesting to see how they have changed, if at all, since 1805," added William.

"William, you remember when the two of us and our friend from South Dakota rafted the Madison a few years ago? I wonder if the Bear Trap was there in 1805. Or *is* there!"

"The Bear Trap?" asked Ellie.

"It's a famous stretch of rapids on the Madison. Big cliffs, fast water. We had a nice lunch on a sandy beach."

Ellie smiled. "Nice lunch, huh? I think I know why you remember it so fondly."

They finished lunch and climbed to the top deck. Paul started the Timer, heading west. The lookouts sat quietly, scanning the countryside with binoculars.

CHAPTER 14

A NEW FRIEND

THE TIMER STAYED low to the ground and followed the terrain's contours. It turned out to be an enjoyable way to travel because they could better appreciate the flowers and wildlife. They passed over creeks so clear they could count every fish against the rocky bottoms. Bob and Paul wanted to stop and fish at several streams that were packed with trout, but William reluctantly said they needed to keep moving. He had not intended to even stop for lunch.

"We need to try to put some distance between us and the other timer. I suspect they're ahead of us, but we really don't know that for sure."

The Timer traveled the rest of the morning, and with the sun high, they ate sandwiches. No one complained about the lunch because no one wanted to take over the preparation, which William and Bob had taken care of. They spent the rest of the afternoon flushing wildlife and enjoying the beautiful weather. They stopped once to watch a bald eagle feed fish, or as Bob called it, "eagle sushi," to her eaglet babies. The nest sat on top of a large, dead tree that had been broken off thirty feet above the ground.

"That is the biggest bird's nest I've ever seen," exclaimed Paul. "It's got to be five feet wide and six feet deep."

"They do build big nests," agreed Bob. "I've seen bigger ones, but that one is big, all right."

As the shadows lengthened, William told Paul to look for a good place to stop for the night. They skirted a forested area that appeared to offer good shelter and cover. A large stream emerged from the forest, and Paul asked if he should follow it back into the trees. Everyone thought this was a good idea, so Paul lowered the Timer almost to the water's surface and followed the stream a hundred yards into the trees. They came to a small clearing that seemed to offer water, dry wood, and concealment. He settled the Timer down, and they started setting up camp.

The four debated whether to have a fire as a cold camp was not very desirable. Paul thought he could build a small one and shield it from anything but a close inspection. William agreed, but it must be small.

"I think I'll take a walk before it gets too dark," said Bob.

"I'm not so sure that's a good idea, Bob," said his brother as he stacked dried branches for their fire.

"I'll be careful and take my gun. I just want to see what's on the other side of this little patch of woods."

He turned and headed west through the forest where big trees surrounded large thickets. By circling the dense areas, Bob made good time and traveled easily and quietly. He had walked about a mile when he stopped and carefully listened. He thought he heard voices. He dropped to the ground and crawled on his hands and knees into a thicket of small bushes and low trees. Feeling well-concealed, he slowly inched his way in the direction he thought the voices might be coming from.

After crawling warily and carefully for several minutes, he came to an opening in the trees. He wiggled under a bush, careful not to break any branches or make any sounds, slowly pushing his way forward.

Well, William wasn't crazy! Fifty yards ahead as he parted some tree limbs, he saw the other timer. Lying very still, he carefully studied the other ship. It was cylindrical, approximately fifty feet long with blunt, almost flat ends. There was a short, stubby conning tower four feet in height near the center from which a ladder extended almost to the ground. The conning tower appeared to be about six feet across with a low railing circling the top with an opening at the ladder. A bright light shone yellow against overhanging branches and seemed to be coming from an open hatch in front of the tower. Bob wasn't sure because it was difficult to tell from his angle beneath the bush.

He counted eight men standing around a fire, smoking and talking in a language he didn't understand. It sounded like German, but he couldn't be positive. One thing he was positive about, though: this was no place he needed to be and no place to be caught by these men.

Bob crawled on hands and knees back through the bushes and toward his friends. He wanted to make better time returning than he had going, so he chose a more open route. He needed to warn the others before they did something to bring attention to themselves.

After losing sight of the other timer, he stood and made faster progress. He had traveled only a short distance when he stumbled into a small clearing. He was so surprised by the sight he almost shouted.

In the clearing was a young Indian boy about his age bound to a tree. He appeared to have been roughly handled as there were numerous cuts and bruises showing on his arms and face. As Bob stepped into the clearing, the boy turned and looked at him. Thankfully, he had made no sound. Rather, a look of fear came over his face. Bob quickly put a finger to his lips. He had no idea whether he would understand the gesture, but it didn't hurt to try. He also smiled in hopes of reassuring the captive. He stretched out his hands, palms up, showing they were empty of any weapons and crept over to the tree to see what was being used to bind the boy's hands. He was restrained with a heavy chain ending in manacles around his wrists. This was going to be tough. Bob had nothing that would cut such thick steel. What was he to do? He couldn't bring himself to leave this young boy like this, but there seemed to be no alternative. He would have to go back to the Timer to get help and tools.

He walked over to the captive and gently patted him on the shoulder. "Don't worry, I have to leave for a few minutes, but I'll be back."

He knew the young man wouldn't understand him but hoped his smile and vocal inflections would be explanation enough. At this, he turned and started across the clearing toward the Timer and his friends.

He had only taken a few steps when he heard the bushes parting behind him. He spun around to see two men entering the clearing just as he was leaving it. Their mouths dropped open, and they stood silently looking back at him. Wanting to act before the spell was broken, Bob snatched out his pistol and shot the closest man in the thigh. He immediately crumpled to the ground with only a moan. He swung the gun on the second man and pulled the trigger. Nothing happened! He had forgotten to check the magazine, and his gun was empty.

CHAPTER 15

THE CHASE

A SMILE REPLACED the fear on the second man's face. He realized Bob's gun wouldn't fire and stepped out into the clearing. He was at least six inches taller than Bob and probably weighed as much. He wore black pants, a black long-sleeved, knit shirt, black boots, and a peaked black cap. His dark complexion, black hair, and large broken nose framed a face with several days of beard, making him appear not only imposing but sinister.

The stranger looked at Bob and spoke in a language Bob could not understand. He quickly realized Bob could not interpret what he said by the puzzled look on his face. "What do we have here? I think I have caught an intruder from the other ship," he said in heavily accented English.

Bob smiled and looked him in the eye. "Maybe I've caught you," he said.

"You're like most Americans. You have an arrogant, big mouth. I think I'll beat you good before I turn you over to the others for their turn." As he spoke these words, he pounded his right fist into his left palm. He was obviously trying to intimidate Bob. This might prove to be unwise.

Bob's face hardened. "You better be a lot tougher than you look if you're going to mess with me!"

"We'll see about that, little man," was the strident reply. And with that, followed by a snarl, the dark giant strode across the center of the clearing and closed in on Bob. He balled up his huge fists and raised them shoulder height in front of his face. Bob stood with his hands by his side and feet placed even and shoulder width apart. His adversary smiled, obviously thinking he had scared the boy into immobility. He drew back his right fist and swung a tremendous blow at Bob's head.

Bob ducked, and the punch whistled just above his head. Then instead of retreating as expected, Bob stepped forward, his left fist slamming into the other man's solar plexus. With a woof of breath, the large man bent forward, pulling his hands to his midsection. Before he could react further, Bob jerked his hands under the other man's arms and rushed him toward the closest tree. With a grunt, Bob lifted his adversary's feet clear of the ground and smashed him into the trunk of the tree. The tree shook, and leaves fluttered down as the man stumbled forward. Bob stepped quickly to his right and drew his right fist back beside his ear. He reached his left hand forward, judging the distance. Then in a flash, he slammed his right fist forward, crashing it into the side of the man's jaw. He quickly drew it back again, but another punch wasn't needed. The man crumpled to the ground, deflated, like a balloon. Bob stood over him for a few seconds just to be sure. The man was out like a light.

Bob now turned to the captive. His eyes were wide with fear and amazement. Bob winked at him, rubbed his knuckles, and started going through the men's pockets. The man he shot lay on his back, eyes closed, snoring lightly. He had nothing in his pockets but a pack of cigarettes and a cheap lighter. In the larger man's breast pocket, Bob found what he was looking for: a ring of keys.

Bob walked over to the young Indian and began trying keys on the manacles. As he tried the third key, the lock popped open with a barely audible click. Bob removed the manacles and gathered the chain in his hands. He had thought of excellent use for it. The former captive struggled to his feet and limped past Bob and started west through the forest. Bob reached out and caught his arm and held it lightly. The Indian's eyes were wide with obvious trepidation as he stared at Bob. Bob smiled as reassuringly as he could manage under the circumstances, released his grip, and patted his new acquaintance on the shoulder. Holding the jingling chain in his left hand, he walked over to the unconscious giant. Reaching down with his right hand, he grabbed the villain's collar and dragged him over to the tree which had formerly held his prisoner. He snapped the manacles to his left wrist then flipped the end of the chain around the tree and back to himself. He snapped that end to the man's other wrist and reached into his pocket, removed a folding knife, and flipped open the blade. The former captive's eye widened as Bob lowered the blade to the chained man's side. He proceeded to split the right sleeve of the new captive's shirt and cut it off at the shoulder. Taking the sleeve and rolling it into a long, black cloth tube, he pried open the giant's mouth and slipped the center of the tube between his teeth. Finishing the job, he pulled the tube firmly behind his prisoner's head and tied the two ends tightly, effectively gagging him. His opponent was now hugging a tree with a gag tied around his head.

Laughing, Bob said to the young Indian, "I know you don't understand me, but he's going to be mad when he wakes up."

The young brave came over and stood next to Bob, obviously admiring his handiwork. Bob glanced over at him and was treated to a nod and a smile.

They both raised their heads as they heard calls from the black timer's vicinity. Without question, they were searching for the two men that now lay unconscious at their feet. The calls became louder and closer. Bob grasped his new friend by the arm and, pulling him the first few steps, led him in the opposite direction. Bob and his new companion moved low and fast through the undergrowth toward the Timer. As Bob ran, he realized the Indian was moving away from him in a more southerly direction. Wishing him well, Bob picked up the pace toward the creek and what he hoped was safety.

He had run only a short distance when shots rang out and bullets whistled through the branches above his head. He dodged left and right to avoid running in a straight line but at the same time running closely in the correct direction. In a minute, this seemed to work as the bullets were not coming as close as before.

Then Bob heard a cry to his left, and turning in that direction, he saw the Indian tumble to the ground clutching his lower left leg.

There was no way Bob would let the Indian be captured again, so he changed direction and ran to the fallen boy. As he reached him, he saw blood seeping from a hole in his left calf. The shot, which seemed to have missed the bone, appeared to have been caused by a small-caliber bullet and did not look too bad. Regardless, he knew it would keep the boy from running very well.

Bob quickly leaned down, caught one arm, lifted, and heaved the injured boy over his shoulder. Other than a slight grunt of pain, the wounded boy made no sound. He's tough, Bob thought as he pushed ahead now with a pain in his side and labored breathing.

With the boy across his shoulder, Bob ran at a trot, directly toward the Timer. He was still ahead of his pursuers but had no idea how far. He also knew that bullets could easily close the gap. Bob made good time even with his load and pumped his left arm as he ran. He remembered a coach once telling him, "You can't move your legs faster than your arms when you run."

As he leaped over a fallen tree, he felt a tug at his left sleeve, followed by a burning sensation in his left bicep. Bob had never been shot before, but he knew he was now. He felt a warm trickle of blood running down his arm. Running this hard probably would exacerbate the bleeding, but there was nothing he could do about that right now. His arm hurt, but it could have been worse. He was thankful it wasn't a leg. He knew had it been his leg, he would have been captured for sure.

Looking ahead, he saw Ellie running toward him. She must have heard the shots and was looking for him. He knew it couldn't be much further to the Timer, but he was tiring fast.

He yelled to Ellie, "Turn around! They aren't too far behind me."

"Do you need help?" she shouted back.

"No, I can manage, but get the Timer ready."

"William got Paul to turn it on at the first shot. It's ready to go," she informed him.

Bob and Ellie rounded a small grove of trees, and the Timer stood only fifty yards ahead. With Ellie running beside him, he reached the ladder and lifted the boy up to William and Paul, who carefully caught him under his arms and gently placed him on the deck.

Bob leaned against the ladder with rasping breath and sweat pouring off his face. He turned to Ellie and motioned her to climb the ladder ahead of him.

She looked at Bob and abruptly blurted out in horror, "Bob, you're shot in two places. You're shot in the arm and the stomach!"

Bob looked down at the front of his shirt and smiled sheepishly. "Just a nick on the arm, the blood on my shirt is from the kid I was carrying."

Just then, they heard distinct shouts. William yelled for them to get aboard as shots began to whiz through the air, with several pinging off the Timer. Ellie scrambled up the ladder, followed more slowly by Bob. As soon as Bob's feet left the ground and both were on the lowest rung, William told Paul to get moving. Paul raised the Timer, moved out over the water, and headed upstream. When the shooting began, William and Paul had already discussed what to do and which way to go. There was no going back for Bob because they might run into the bad guys first. They decided when Bob got back, it was best to continue upstream because they might run into the other timer going back the way they had come.

This proved to be a good plan.

"Looking back, I think it was definitely a good idea to come this way. We've run into trouble, but going back that way would have been bigger trouble," Bob said as he stared downstream.

Behind them, they could see a spotlight swinging back and forth, probing the dark. They watched as the light beam steadied and focused down the corridor of trees. The other timer was several hundred yards behind, but it was following their trail.

William pulled out a nightscope and trained it at the spotlight's bright glare, and after a few seconds, he had the other timer in focus. "It appears to have a conning tower roughly the shape of a World War II submarine. The prow is blunt, almost flat. One thing I'm thankful for is that it doesn't have a deck gun."

By now, Ellie also had her nightscope up. "I guess they didn't think it needed to be streamlined. Maybe that shape gives them more room inside."

"That may explain the larger crew I saw earlier. They have at least twice as many people as we do," Bob said as he tore his left sleeve open in order to survey his wound.

About that time, they could see blinking lights on top of the other craft's conning tower. This was quickly followed by the unmistakable hum of bullets whizzing by them. None hit the Timer or them, but they cut through the leaves and branches all around, resulting in confetti of pulverized leaves raining down on the deck. Also, they were now caught in the unblinking spotlight's glare. The harsh beam of white light threw the Timer's shadow out in front of them in the race up the stream. The trees on each side were now muted walls, indistinct in the mixture of light and shadow, but seemed as solid as buildings on a city street.

With alacrity, William ordered everyone below because it was getting too dangerous to stay completely exposed on the upper deck. He remained on top with Paul as they maneuvered down the now narrowing twin rows of trees. Each bank seemed to be squeezing in on them as the trees got closer. Paul crouched down with only his head visible while William lay flat on his stomach, alternating facing forward or looking back over his shoulder.

"William, I don't know how much longer we're going to be able to fit through these trees. The stream is definitely getting narrower."

William leaned closer to Paul's ear in order to be heard. "Unfortunately, that's not the only problem, Paul. They are faster than we are." He had noticed the gap between them closing. Occasionally, a bullet would ricochet off their hull. The shots didn't seem to do any damage, but it was still scary. So far, they had been extremely lucky no one had been hit.

William knew they had to figure a way out of this predicament, and fast. If they continued down this stream, they would either get squeezed out by the closing trees or hit the open range. If they hit the open range, the other timer would run them down.

As they continued upstream, the banks remained low, but the screen of trees remained thick and almost down to the waterline. William had an idea. It was a long shot, but it seemed an alternative to getting caught. It was worth a try.

"Paul, some of these trees have branches that start ten feet or so off the ground. The next time you see an opening as wide as the Timer, we might be able to force our way through between the ground and the lower branches. I don't know what else we can do."

With that, William and Paul began to scan the banks. The full moon helped. They got at least one break: the stream began to curve and meander so they were not constantly in the spotlight's glare. William was surprised that the bright light made it more difficult to see, not easier.

Five minutes later, Paul turned to William and said in an excited voice, "William, look over there. What do you think?"

William looked in the direction Paul was indicating and saw two trees, standing well apart, with branches that started twelve to fifteen feet above the ground. That was part of what they were look- ing for. Complicating things were bushes filling up the space from the ground to the lower branches.

"Paul, do you think we can break through those bushes?"

"I don't know. I'll do whatever you say."

The other timer was now only a hundred and fifty yards back and the gunfire more accurate. The distance closing fast. William decided they had no choice but to give it a try.

William looked down the hatch and said, "Everyone, hold on. It may get a little rocky here for a few seconds."

"Okay, Paul. Give it the gun, and let's see what we can do." William grabbed hold of the railing, ducked his head, and knelt on the deck.

Paul wheeled the Timer to the left and lowered it until it almost touched the water. He then backed it up until it brushed the trees on the opposite bank. Glancing sideward at William, he gave the Timer full power. The Timer leaped the short distance in a second and crashed into the bushes, which held for a few seconds then parted and gave way. The Timer again leaped forward for another twenty feet then came to a crashing halt. A heavy branch had caught the top railing, becoming wedged, and held them fast.

"Back up, Paul!" yelled William.

"I've tried, and it won't move."

"Get up here, Bob…quick!" commanded William as he reached down and took his brother's hand, pulling him through the hatch.

"I know you're hurt, but you're the strongest one of us, and we need you right now. We have to lift this branch high enough to let us slip the railing beneath it."

Bullets were now flying uncomfortably close. The other timer was trying to keep the spotlight on them, but the intervening trees were making that difficult. Leaves began to rain down again as the firing intensified. In a moment, their adversaries would be even with the Timer's entrance to the woods.

Moving to the front, William and Bob leaned over and grasped the offending limb. They struggled to lift it, but after a few seconds, they managed to raise it several inches above the railing.

William turned to Paul, "Move the Timer slowly forward. Bob and I will try to walk back with the branch. We've got to do something."

The two boys stood behind the branch, bent over, and, grasping it, lifted for all they were worth. They strained to their limit, raised the branch clear of the railing and slowly walked backward toward the rear of the Timer with their heavy load.

As they approached the railing, Paul knelt, and the branch passed just above his head. The Timer was slowly moving forward and the branch slowly moving back. They now were getting close to the rear railing.

Sweat poured down William's face as he looked at his brother. "Stop before we get to the railing so we can swap sides."

As they reached the rear railing, Paul stopped the Timer and asked, "Do you want me to help you?"

Bob looked up with an expression of pain and determination on his face. "Paul, get ready to lift from that side. William, get ready to join him. I think I can hold it while the two of you get into position."

True to his word, Bob held up the heavy branch alone while William hastily crawled under it to the other side. Paul swiveled out of his seat, stepping up to join William as they cradled the branch against their thighs. Bob quickly squeezed under the branch, took it in his hands, and yelled, "Go, Paul!"

With the screeching sound of tortured metal, the Timer broke loose. Cheering, Paul quickly steered it through the remaining bushes and the last thirty feet to the freedom of the open plains. The railing was bent on both sides in several places, but they were free!

They heard screams and yells from the other craft, and suddenly, a blazing spotlight illuminated the Timer once again. There were more shouts and then the crashing sound of metal striking wood. The spotlight veered off to the side, cloaking them in darkness again. The enemy timer's shape was not conducive to following their path, and it had been stopped cold. They were saved again!

"Those guys are going to have to cut their way through more than one big branch." Laughed William.

There was more shouting and yelling, followed by ineffective shots fired in their general direction. Regardless, they were safe, and Paul had the Timer moving rapidly away across the vast plains. Now, finally, they all signed with relief.

"Let's don't do that again anytime soon," William said, smiling as he turned and looked at Bob, who sat on the deck with his back against the railing. Blood had run down his arm and stained his sleeve, but it obviously didn't bother him. Bob smiled back and gave his big brother a quick thumbs-up.

William patted Paul on the back. "Great job! Set a course due south and let's get away from here."

"And may we never see those guys again," replied Paul with relief on his face.

Paul swung the Timer to the left, heading south, intending to turn southwest later and move toward what would become Idaho. Everyone but Paul looked back in the direction of the other timer. They could see wildly swinging beams of light from the spotlights that had so recently trapped them in their glare. They could also still hear the distant shouts from angry voices. The voices soon faded out, but they watched the spotlights for another half hour. The distance between them and their adversaries rapidly widened, and they were able to sit back and relax for the first time since the chase began.

"I bet they won't try that again." Bob laughed. "I'm thinking they are going to have to retrace their steps back to the point where I bumped into that big, dumb-looking guy."

"Just how big was this big, dumb-looking guy?" asked William.

Upon hearing the answer and the details of the fight, everyone was suitably impressed with how Bob had handled himself.

"Bob, why don't you pick a little smaller opponent next time?" Paul said.

"Don't worry; I wouldn't have picked him this time. I do think he was surprised I wasn't scared of him."

William moved beside Paul. "Swing back to the west and let's go to the Madison River. It's the best way to get through the Gravelly and Madison Ranges. If we don't do that, it will be hit-and-miss to find our way through the mountains. We could do it, but it might take a while. It might take a long while."

With that, William then went below, and he and Ellie began tending to the two wounded boys. Thankfully, they each had only flesh wounds and no broken bones.

As Ellie approached the young Indian, he scooted back against the wall. She carried antiseptic and bandages and spoke soothingly to him as she gently dabbed at the wound. He winced once then let her clean the wound and bandage his leg. He showed no further sign of pain or any emotion. He was very quiet.

Ellie said, "Wonder what is going through his mind right now? He's wounded, with strangers and on a flying machine!"

At this same time, William was working on his brother. The bullet had entered his arm just above the bicep and had made a small hole going in and a slightly larger one coming out. He cleaned the wound, swabbed it with antiseptic, and wrapped the bandage around Bob's arm.

"Bob, your arm is so big I'm going to use up an entire roll of our medical tape. You cannot get shot again! It's too tedious for me treating you and uses up way too much of our medical supplies."

"Bro, trust me, it wasn't my idea. I'll try to dodge better next time."

Ellie stood up having finished part of her nursing duties. William and Bob looked over and took an inventory of her patient. He appeared to be about five feet, eight inches tall, was slender, and probably weighed about one hundred and thirty pounds. He was lean and muscular with skin the color of mahogany. Striking with his dark-brown eyes and shiny, jet-black hair, he wore buckskin leggings and a beaded, torn buckskin shirt. He had a leather band around his neck, and his hair hung loose on his shoulders. Any hair ornamentation he might have had had been lost while he was a captive. His face was bruised and battered; there was a cut above his left eye, and he had a split lower lip.

Ellie peered closely at his face and began cleaning the cut. She was very gentle and careful to make no sudden moves. He was very stoic and barely blinked as she placed a butterfly bandage over the wound. She stood back and appeared satisfied with her work.

Reaching out, she patted down one corner of the bandage. "I wish we could get him a shot of antibiotics."

Placing a hand on her shoulder, William said, "You did great. I suspect if you approached him with a hypodermic needle, all of us, including Bob, couldn't hold him. I bet he has had enough cuts and scrapes in his life to be immune to every germ out here."

The young Indian touched the bandage over his eye and then leaned back against the bulkhead. He stared defiantly around at the others and crossed his arms across his chest with clenched fists. Ellie said these were classic signs of defensiveness and feigned toughness. She knew they had to somehow break through this and put him more at ease.

Ellie turned to Bob. "He's got to be hungry and thirsty. Let me see if I can get him to drink a little water and eat something."

Ellie went to the small, built-in galley and poured a green, plastic cup full of water. She raised it to her mouth and took a small sip. She then extended it to the newcomer. He greedily licked his lips and took the cup from her hand, rubbing the plastic with his fingers and sliding them around its smooth surface.

"Never seen plastic," whispered Bob.

He then raised the cup to his lips and tentatively sipped, quickly gulped, emptying the cup. Ellie refilled it. He again drank the water down in a flash, repeating this three times. After the third time, he carefully placed the cup down on the deck.

Seeing his thirst was quenched, Bob reached into his pocket and removed a candy bar. He partially unwrapped the paper and took a small bite. He stretched out his hand, offering the remainder to the Indian. Taking the candy, he looked it over very closely, and finally, he touched it to his tongue. He looked pleasantly surprised and then smiled broadly as he took a bite. He rapidly consumed the sweet treat, eating only a little of the paper in the process.

Laughing, Bob noted, "I have never seen a Milky Way enjoyed more."

Ellie smiled at William and Bob. "The way to a man's heart."

CHAPTER 16

THE NAME

THEY WERE DISCUSSING their narrow escape when the young Indian reached out and stroked Ellie's hair, causing her to jump in surprise. He slowly rubbed the strands of hair between his fingers. Stopping, he looked closely at his fingers. Obviously, he was checking to see if the color had come off.

"He's never seen red hair," Ellie whispered softly.

He touched her hair again then sat back and looked at Bob. After studying him for a long minute, he moved gingerly across the floor and sat down cross-legged in front of him. He raised his arms and extended them toward Bob with palms up. He got an earnest look on his face and began to address him. He spoke in a slightly singsong voice for almost two minutes, then with a nod of his head, he sat back on his heels, his eyes never leaving Bob's face.

Bob smiled at the others. "I think I've just been thanked."

Bob reached out and placed his hand on the other boy's shoulder and said a very sincere, "Thank you."

His new friend took his right index finger and poked Bob in the chest several times. After studying Bob for a minute, he then tried to reach around Bob's uninjured bicep and smiled when his fingers did not come close to touching. He spread his hands wide then brought them in till they were touching to outsides of Bob's shoulders. Holding his hands steady and apart, he turned to the others to show them how broad Bob was. A smile broke out on his face, and a small laugh rumbled from his stomach.

"He's feeling better. I guess since I'm the only one around here that isn't strange, abnormal, or has funny-colored hair. That fascinates him," said Bob with a smile.

Ellie looked at her friends and said, "I guess it's about time for the 'Me Jane, you Tarzan' routine." I want to see if I can communicate with him on a slightly higher level than winks and nods. He may be able to help us through this new country we're about to enter. We may need all the help we can get."

Everyone thought this a good idea and gathered around as Ellie sat down next to her new student. She began working with him, and to the amazement of the others, they soon knew several words of each other's language. He had a quick mind and knew the name of a of things like caps, boots, and socks in only a few minutes. His pronunciation of "candy" bar did bring out chuckles of mirth. This went on for over an hour and only stopped when Ellie's yawns kept interrupting the lesson. It had been time well-spent.

Bob spread an extra sleeping bag out on the deck. Unzipping it, he showed their new friend how to slide his feet into the foot. When he had done so, Bob began to zip up the bag. This brought a look of alarm on the boy's face, and he scrambled backward out of the bag. He apparently felt as if he were being restrained again. When Ellie, William, and Paul climbed into their bags, he relaxed. Bob coaxed him back into his sleeping bag and left the zipper unzipped, which seemed to work much better. Putting his hands behind his head, he relaxed, laid back, and, in no time, was sound asleep.

The next day dawned clear and bright after a midnight rain. Dew sparkled like glitter on the leaves, bushes, and flowers as the sun rose. Paul had parked the Timer in a meadow a hundred yards up a small stream that fed into the river. Deciding against a fire, and thus having a cold breakfast, caused Bob's usual complaints about the food quality; however, when threatened with becoming the full-time cook, he recanted. He said it really wasn't that bad even though he was still a little hungry.

"You may not have liked cold oatmeal, but you ate three bowls," his brother pointed out.

"Taking one for the team," was the wry response.

Ellie checked all the bandages and decided to change only the young Indian's. His had bled through the wrapping during the night. With part speaking and part sign language, Ellie told him he was moving around too much. She spread a tarp on the ground and had him elevate his leg over a fallen tree. They could all tell he thought this very odd, but he complied. She then removed the bandage and was relieved to see no sign of inflammation or infection. She tossed the old bandage on the ground. Paul quickly picked it up and buried it. Ellie wound a new bandage around his leg, taping it securely. Moving on to Bob, she inspected his bandage. Seeing only a small spot of blood on each side, she decided to leave it alone. This relieved Bob as he didn't want it "fooled with," as he so inelegantly put it.

Ellie turned back to her other patient, sitting on the fallen tree. She pointed to herself and said, "Ellie." She then pointed to him, held her arms out palms up, and looked at him inquiringly.

He got a puzzled look on his face, as well, and said nothing.

Ellie again pointed to herself and said her name. She pointed to Bob and said his name. Her eyes widened as her pupil touched his chest, speaking several words. Surely, one of these words must be his name?

Ellie turned to the others. "I think he just called himself Spearmint."

William laughed. "Obviously, he didn't call himself Spearmint."

Stifling a laugh, Ellie retorted, "Maybe not, but it sure sounded like it."

"Well, we can't call him Spearmint, that just wouldn't be right," said William. "Let's call him Spear. It's pretty close and it seems to fit."

Ellie reached over and touched her finger to his chest and said, "Spear."

He smiled in agreement and vigorously nodded his head.

Bob looked over. "I'm glad we finally have a name to work with. I'm tired of referring to him as 'He' or he as 'Him.' Spear? Spear! I like it… Spear it is."

Spear and the others enjoyed a breakfast of oatmeal, raisins, and nuts. Thinking he would spice up Spear's oatmeal, William put a spoonful of brown sugar on top. Spear, with the tip of his tongue, touched the sugar, continued until all the sugar was gone. He looked up and smiled broadly. William made a mental note to stir it in next time. He suspected the Indians of the western plain had little idea or concept of something sweet. He could think of only two possibilities: berries and honey. Neither would be as sweet as the brown sugar.

After breakfast, William and Paul inspected the Timer in detail. The bullets made no impression on the exterior. They didn't know if this was because the Timer was hard or because the bullets were small caliber. Either way, unless the other timer had a bigger gun, they would probably be okay. The only damage they could find was on several handrail sections. They were bent but unbroken. In places, the paint was scraped down to bare metal. It had the look and sheen of pewter. This damage had happened when they plowed through trees and brush to safety. They pronounced the Timer safe and reliable.

William told the others to get ready to move. "If they've been moving at night, then we are going to move during the day. At least that's the plan right now. We just need to be vigilant."

Bob volunteered to go ahead to the river and make sure the other timer was not in sight. He walked slowly along the riverbank, sticking to the trees as much as possible. As he approached the river, he got down on his hands and knees and crawled into a thicket overhanging the bank. Now he could stand up and look through the tangle of limbs, surveying the river both upstream and downstream. He saw nothing. Turning slowly, he quietly retraced his steps to the others and told them the coast was clear.

The others waited on top of the Timer. Paul quickly dropped the Timer to the ground to pick up Bob. Bob clambered up the ladder, and they drove down the small stream to where it intersected with the Madison. Here, they took several minutes just to make sure the enemy timer wasn't in hiding or coming around the last bend in the river. Seeing no one, Paul tucked in as close as he dared to the bank, and away, they went.

The river meandered through a narrow, flat valley of small meadows that were strewn with wildflowers. There were colors of purple, red, blue, yellow, gold, and white. Bob pointed out a taller flower with brilliant red pedals. It was his favorite, the Indian Paintbrush. They passed above a rocky terrain and over splashing rapids. When they entered one narrow canyon, they saw mountain goats grazing high on steep slopes. All in all, they made good time and enjoyed themselves.

Everyone stayed on top of the Timer, lying down or sitting back against the railing. Ellie made Spear prop his leg over the railing which was cushioned with a folded tarp. She wanted to elevate the leg to help prevent or reduce any further bleeding.

Paul looked back over his shoulder. "What a great way to travel!"

"Flying over this beautiful country in an airplane wouldn't do this scenery justice," said William as he surveyed the surrounding landscape.

Bob and Ellie made sandwiches with canned ham, handing them up through the hatch. Spear had never eaten a sandwich or tasted mustard, but he seemed to catch on rapidly. William showed him how to hold the sandwich together and not eat it piece by piece. They ate as Paul flew them down the Madison, wanting to cover as many miles as possible. William pointed out that there were about as many hours of daylight as night. If they got ahead to begin with, they would probably stay ahead.

"I have another idea of something we might consider as I think we now have plenty of time. How about a little adventure attached to the big adventure?"

Bob looked over at his brother. "What do you have in mind, William?"

"Paul, Ellie, have you ever heard of Alder Gulch?"

"Nope," Paul answered without looking around.

"Me either," replied Ellie, looking bewildered.

With a tone that showed he was not surprised, William said, "Alder Gulch was the site of the greatest discovery of placer gold deposits in history. We are only going to be a few hours away. I thought we might go over and see what it looked like before it was discovered. You might even get to pan a little gold."

"Can we find it?" asked his brother.

"I think so. It's directly west of Ennis, Montana."

With a chuckle, Bob responded, "William, I don't think Ennis was there in 1805."

"I know, but I think we can figure out where it will be. Ennis is located on a big bend in the river. There is at least a half-mile-long bulge to the west at Ennis. I believe if we watch the compass carefully, we can spot it."

"I'm game if everyone else is. Let's see if we can find it. What do you, guys, think about it?'

"What is placer gold?" asked Ellie.

"Okay, to simplify," said William, "it's where gold has been moved from a vein or mother lode by some force like water or even a glacier. Frequently, miners found it panning in sand or gravel deposits. It's usually found in a valley where the gold kind of fed to the bottom."

With a big smile, Paul added, "Or found in a gulch?"

Running his fingers back through his hair, William smiled, "Actually, a gulch is nothing but a steep, narrow ravine. Do we want to go?"

Both Paul and Ellie nodded vigorously. It was obvious: the thought of gold excited everyone.

"Who discovered Alder Gulch?" inquired Ellie.

"Interesting story," said William as he pulled some thread off the frayed cuff of his overalls.

"Some prospectors were on the way to the Yellowstone Country when a band of Indians jumped them. They managed to hide in what turned out to be Alder Gulch. While hiding out, they found gold. They were going to try to keep it secret, but as usual, word got out. In just a few months, thousands of people came there searching for gold."

"Alder, that's a funny name. Where did it come from?" asked Ellie.

"The alder is a tree that grows there. I suspect we'll see plenty of them in a while," answered William.

Hours later, after they passed through an area where the river had numerous channels, it began a slight turn to the west. This turn continued for at least a quarter of a mile. They then traveled due south, and the compass needle began to swing back to the east. William told Paul to stop.

"Okay, if everyone agrees, I think this will be Ennis. I say let's get Paul to turn west and see what we can find."

"How far is it to Alder Gulch, William?" asked Paul.

"I'm not sure. Do you know, Bob?"

Bob paused for a minute then replied, "I think it's fifteen to twenty miles to the Virginia City location then not far beyond that. We can probably get close in a couple of hours."

"Well, if that's right, we should know fairly quickly if this is the correct turn," said William. "If it's the wrong turn, it won't take us long to come back."

"William and I have been there several times, and I think we can recognize the right area if this is it."

"Maybe," his brother added.

"If it is, maybe we can find some gold," said Ellie.

"Right, I expect to," agreed a seemly confident Bob.

CHAPTER 17

———⌢———

PANNING FOR GOLD

PAUL STEERED THEM across fields, over gullies, and up hills. A little over an hour later, William called for a halt. "Bob, look around and see what you think. There's something familiar about this area."

Leaning his knees against the railing, Bob looked in all directions. "Well, it sure looks different without the buildings, but I think this is it. All the hills seem to be in the right places, just no streets and no buildings." Pointing off to their right, he added, "That little creek looks about the right size and place as the one that ran through town."

"The one that ran next to the old brewery?"

"Yep, that's the one."

Paul turned to William. "If this is Virginia City, which way do we go from here?"

"Okay, put us on a northwest heading, Paul. If we're right, we'll pass through the future homes of ten small communities in the next twelve to fifteen miles."

"Will do."

"Ten towns in fifteen miles?" Ellie asked Bob in an astonished voice.

"All of them kind of popped out of the ground when gold was discovered in 1863. Virginia City was even the territorial capital for a while and had a population of ten thousand. It was a really a booming area. Hopefully, in the next few miles, we will start moving downhill. If we do, we should be over Alder Gulch."

Paul slowed to ten miles per hour and began angling off to the northwest. As predicted, after a few miles, the land started to drop off slightly. Soon, they were moving down a long, rugged, rocky valley. The top of the ridge was lined with alder trees. It appeared to William and Bob that they had found the fabled Alder Gulch. Now all they had to do was find some gold. William and Bob leaned against the Timer's railing, weighing the pros and cons of various locations. After much head nodding and discussion, Bob stood up and went below deck while his brother remained topside.

William pointed off to their left and turned to Paul. "Pull over to that little creek and set her down. We think that's as likely a spot as any."

Paul steered, found a fairly flat area, and dropped the Timer, light as a feather, to the ground.

"Paul, you have really mastered flying the Timer. You're getting better and better," said William, patting him on the back.

"Thanks. It's just a matter of practice. Like anything else, the more you do it, the better you get. I really enjoy it."

"We probably don't all need to be off the Timer without a lookout in this country. I'll take the first shift and stay up here while the rest of you hunt for gold," William said.

"Well, William, neither Paul nor I know the first thing about hunting for gold. What do we need to do and how will we know when we've found it?"

"Bob is below getting something that might help you. Trust me. With just a little help and a little knowledge, you'll know gold when you see it."

About that time, Bob's head poked up through the hatch. "Guess what I've found?" he asked.

Clapping her hands with excitement, Ellie asked, "What!"

"I've got two gold pans."

Bob held up two metal pans about eighteen inches round. "William and I think they're original gold pans from the 1800s, but we don't know for sure. We asked Dailey, but even he doesn't know. I bet Dad got these at some point in the past."

The two pans were iron with copper linings. Neither had handles, and nothing was fancy about them. These particular pans had no depression in the center, making panning a more delicate operation. You had to be careful to swish out only the water and sediment and not the gold.

"Do they come with instructions?" Paul asked, laughing.

"No, but brother Bob is an excellent gold-panning instructor. Watch what he does. If there's gold in that gravel and rock, you'll find it for sure."

Handing one of the pans to Ellie and keeping the other for himself, Bob quickly climbed down the ladder. Ellie and Paul followed. Walking over to the small stream, he turned to his two friends and said, "Watch and learn from the master."

While all this was going on, Spear was leaning over the railing and watching with rapt attention. He seemed to be hanging on Bob's every word and action. He was to get his turn.

Bob knelt beside the small stream and scooped up some gravel and rocks. "Keep in mind, gold is heavy and sinks down between rocks. This is a very rocky stream, so we may need to move some of the rocks aside to get to the gravel more easily."

Getting a pan three quarters full of sediment, he slowly began to swirl it in circles. Occasionally, he would dip one side of the pan and spill out water and gravel. After a few minutes of this, he stuck his finger in the remaining gravel and stirred it around and said with great disgust, "Nothing!"

"Let me try, let me try," said Ellie as she moved several small rocks and scooped up a pan of gravel. Mimicking Bob, she swirled the pan and began emptying water and gravel. Stopping every few minutes, she dug her fingers into the remaining sediment, hoping to spot a piece of gold.

"Keep going. You need to dump a little more gravel to really see if you have anything," said Bob, smirking slightly and with condescension in his voice.

After a few more minutes of water and gravel dumping, Ellie stopped, staring carefully at her pan. Slowly stirring the sediment with her fingers, she leaned closer until her nose was only a foot from the pan. "What is this, a shiny pebble?" she said, reaching into the pan with her thumb and index finger and retrieving a small stone.

"Let's see," said Bob, holding out his large hand. Ellie gently placed it in Bob's right palm. He drew it closer to his eyes. "That's not a pebble, that's a nugget! And it's a really nice and big nugget!" Bob cradled his forehead in his left hand as he surveyed Ellie's find. "Beginner's luck," he snorted.

"Yea!" Ellie said enthusiastically and continued hunting through the remaining gravel in her pan.

Bob laughed, his good humor returning, held out the nugget, and carefully placed it in Ellie's hand.

"Can you feel how heavy it is?" he asked.

Moving her hand slowly up and down, she replied, "It really is amazingly heavy!"

"Okay, new master, you and Paul go and find some more."

Paul took the other pan and moved upstream. He said he wanted to get the nuggets before they washed down to Ellie. Bob followed him to the new location. Between them, they moved a large pile of rocks out of the stream and onto the bank. This gave Paul a four-by-four-foot opening and access to the gravel and dirt below.

Under Bob's supervision, Paul scooped, swirled, and swished the sediment. After an hour, he had several small nuggets although none as big as Ellie's. He also had found golden flecks. Bob thought he had also found some dust, but they couldn't be sure. All in all, Paul was pleased.

Then it was Spear's turn to try gold mining. With a little help from William and Bob, Spear climbed down the ladder and limped over to the stream. Ellie thought it a bad idea but finally agreed that a few minutes of panning probably wouldn't hurt.

Bob quickly cleared some rocks from the stream next to a flat area on the bank. Spear sat down with his injured leg on the bank and his other foot in the water. It was awkward, but by bending at the waist, he was able to scoop up gravel in his pan. He then began to swirl the water, letting a little trickle over the side. He had obviously been watching the others and was also quite good at it. After only a few minutes, he turned and held out his pan to Ellie. She took the pan in her hands, sat down cross-legged next to Spear, and examined the contents.

"Look at this guy!" Reaching up with the gold pan, she handed it to Bob, who was standing behind her.

"I can't believe it. I'm definitely no longer the master." Bob handed the pan to William, who stared in disbelief. There were three nuggets, all equal to or bigger in size than Ellie's. There were also numerous gold flecks a line of fine, shiny gold dust. Spear had been a good prospector and made an excellent find.

William looked thoughtful for a full minute. "You know, his spot is at the outside curve of slight bend in the stream. I bet that gold kind of filtered out to this place in the stream and got trapped in the rocks."

Looking perplexed, Bob said, "Whatever the reason, he did really well. I think everyone has done well. Now let me try my hand at it again. Surely, I can find a little gold."

Bob was correct. He found a little gold. Pushing his few scraps of gold around, he remarked, "If all of us can find gold, is it any wonder the miners took ten million dollars' worth out in the first year? There must be lots of gold here about."

Thoughtfully, William replied, "There really was lots of gold taken out of this valley. Bob and I have ridden through here, and on both sides of the road as far as you can see are piles of rocks. It looked like the miners turned over every rock in Alder Gulch looking for gold. It's a pretty amazing sight."

"This seems like a pretty isolated place. What if we bed down here for the night?" asked Paul as he perused the valley.

"I think that's a good idea," said William. "It's going to be dark soon, and there is no reason to be moving over rough country that we don't know. It's not like flying over a nice, flat river."

With Paul and Bob gathering wood, Spear soon had a small fire going. They placed a large pot of water on rocks positioned around the fire. Once the water was bubbling, they dropped in some dried soup mix, which soon filled the air with the delicious aroma of vege-table soup. They quickly consumed it; getting seconds was the order of the day. Even Bob agreed it was a good meal though he was not a big soup fan.

Spreading sleeping bags on top of inflatable pads, and on top of these sleeping bags, the friends gathered around the fire. Paul and Bob continued to feed sticks into the blaze for another hour as the conversation slowly died away. Finally, the only sound to be heard was gentle breathing from all sides. The sky was inky black, with a scattering of white stars. There was no moon to be seen that night.

They were up with the sun the next morning. The others teased Bob and William as their bear spray rolled out from the tops of their sleeping bags. Unless they were sleeping on the deck or in the Timer, they kept it close at hand each night. This was a habit picked up during their summers spent volunteering with the Forest Service. You probably will never need it, but to need it and not to have it would be really bad.

Sleeping next to the stream made breakfast prep easy. They fanned fire coals red, added more wood, and were soon ready to cook. The cleaned pot from the night before was now ready to handle today's breakfast of oatmeal with dried apple mixed in. That, com-bined with Paul's concoction of strong, black coffee, served to wake everyone up. William said it was amazing how fast they could get used to strong, black coffee. Most had preferred sugar and cream, but they were trying to ration both, especially the sugar. Without sugar, there would not be the occasional dessert. Again, because of the proximity of the water, they were able to get everything rubbed with sand and washed clean in just a few minutes. It also afforded Spear and Ellie the opportunity to each find several small nuggets, which they did. Everything was packed away, including their recently found gold. The gold nuggets, flakes, and dust were placed in a Tupperware community container with a tight-fitting top.

Looking at the container and shaking the gold, William remarked, "You know, this much gold would have kept a miner in beans and coffee for months in 1863. It might have kept him here long enough to be one of those that hit the bonanza and went home rich."

"It's almost enough to make you want to hide that gold under a rock and let one of those guys from 1863 find it," said Bob.

"One big problem," said his brother. "Dad didn't like leaving things from our time in another time period where it didn't fit. I doubt much Tupperware was sold in 1863."

"You're right, and if I poured it under a rock, in sixty years it would probably be scattered all over the place. I would rather make one miner happy than tease several into thinking they were about to hit a strike."

"Well, if finding gold makes you a gold miner, then I guess you, guys, even you, Bob, are gold miners. Having mastered that, I say let's head back the way we came. Once we hit the Madison River, I think we should drive south. Let's see if we can retrace our steps, and if we can, I'll see what you all think when we get there. Do we need to head south or go straight in?"

"Do you think we should have dropped bread crumbs on the way here, like Hansel and Gretel?" asked Bob.

"I was pretty careful to keep up with the general headings coming over here. I probably won't hit the exact the spot we left from, but I shouldn't miss it by too much," said Paul.

Sitting down on the front of the Timer, William said, "Truthfully, if you fly due east, I don't think you could miss the Madison if you tried."

Paul gave the Timer full throttle, and they rapidly covered ground back to their starting point. They had traveled about thirty minutes when, suddenly, Spear made a grunting noise and pointed directly in front of them. Ellie leaned down and quietly said something in his ear. Turning his head, he replied, but no one except Ellie could hear what he said.

Turning to the others, Ellie said, "Spear says he can see smoke."

Ellie and the other three stared in the direction Spear had pointed but saw nothing.

Shaking his head and speaking to Paul, William said, "I don't see a thing, but slow down and move a little more south. We should still hit the Madison, and I guess it's better to be safe than sorry."

Less than ten minutes later, Bob spoke up, "I can see what Spear is talking about, I think. There is a thin trail of smoke rising off to our left center at about eleven o'clock."

In another few minutes, everyone could see a thin column of white smoke rising through the trees. Had they continued their course, they might have missed it entirely until the last minute and driven almost directly over the source of the smoke.

Ellie again leaned down, speaking to Spear. He turned and said something to the others. As it was in his language, they didn't understand a word.

Ellie said, "I told him he must have eyes like an eagle to see that smoke so far away. He said some in his tribe called him Long Looker because of his fantastic vision."

"I can believe it," replied Bob. "I thought I could see a long way, but he puts me to shame. He could see that smoke over a mile and a half before I could."

Still marveling at Spear's vision, the crew gathered in the front of the Timer, looking for the Madison River. After a few minutes, they could see the Madison's gleam through a grove of Aspens directly in front of them. Skirting to the south, Paul drove to a marshy area adjacent to the bank, hovering five feet above the ground.

"Discussion time," said William. "Maybe the other timer is following us down this river. If we change rivers, perhaps we can lose them. They may not be following us at all, but we left them angry. I bet they're looking somewhere for us."

"Especially my buddy," added Bob with a laugh.

"Let's do it then," said William. "I have another reason or two I'll talk about later."

The others nodded in agreement.

CHAPTER 18

ON TO YELLOWSTONE

THEY FOLLOWED THE river for the rest of the afternoon. It was as pleasant a day as any of them could remember. The warm breezes, bright sunshine, and blue skies put everyone in a good mood. Paul said that flying low over occasional rapids was almost like riding a raft. Unless there were large rocks, he had become so skilled that he could drop the Timer within a few feet of the waves.

It was thrilling for all but William who kept saying, "Not too close, Paul, not too close."

Late that afternoon, they felt they'd gone far enough for the day. After scouting the area, Paul pushed the Timer through some small trees into a clearing that was a short distance from the riverbank. He parked under the overhang of some large trees on the side farthest from the river. After dropping the Timer to the ground, they cut some lower limbs from nearby trees and laid them against the Timer's side. This concealed their craft from only the closest inspections by prying eyes.

Ellie and William erected a small tarp as a screen and scavenged some of the plentiful dry wood littering the river bank. Spear sat next to the woodpile and built a fire. He was by now in charge of fire building and could make one that was nearly smokeless, and what wispy, white smoke there was seemed to settle into the trees so to not give away their location.

Ellie and William made a soup using river water, canned chicken, and dried noodles. The buttery noodles and tender chicken drew rave reviews as almost everyone was a little tired of fish. Spear really enjoyed the variety of new foods. He was getting something new and exotic daily. Ellie noted the likelihood that there had not been much variation in his diet over the years.

"He has probably eaten a ton of buffalo meat in his life," she said, with a hint of distaste in the squint of her eyes.

Ellie said she was very proud of Spear. For someone exposed to new foods, new language, new technology, and almost new every-thing, he was adapting quite fast. She said he was very bright and learning English at a rapid pace. He now knew everyone's name but was insistent on calling Ellie "Flaming Hair." The fascination with her brilliant, red hair continued. After initially correcting Spear a few times, she gave up and accepted her new name. Flaming Hair it was and would be. Bob questioned Ellie's translation, wondering if it was Carrot Top. Ellie was not amused.

There was one thing that totally confounded Spear. He was totally transfixed by the Timer's ability to fly. Each morning as Paul lifted the Timer airborne, he clung tightly to the railing and looked down as the ground receded. He never seemed to tire of that and the Timer's ability to move so smoothly through the air. Paul even tried to get him to steer a little bit, but he would have no part of it. Ellie indicated that as best she could tell, he thought flying to be some-what magical, and was quite in awe.

To avoid the other timer, the friends decided to maintain watch each night. Between 9:00 p.m. and 6:00 a.m., each of the original crew had two-hour-and-fifteen-minute watches. They excluded Spear for the time being because they weren't sure how he would react if he spotted his former captors. They were afraid he might shout or scream and give away their location. Ellie said she was work-ing on it, and he would soon be able to take a turn. She contended anything he might say upon seeing the other timer would be out of anger, not fear.

The night passed uneventfully. The changing of the watches went smoothly although Paul said he had to poke Bob three times to finally wake him.

"And he poked me hard too. I was really sleeping well and dreaming about one of Dailey's big breakfasts. Let me tell you what all we had." This was greeted by a chorus of no as the others did want to hear or think about anything other than oatmeal.

After having their ever-present oatmeal, the friends loaded up the Timer. It was time to get going again. They climbed to the Timer's deck, settling into their personal spots.

William walked over to stand beside Paul. "Let me tell you what I have in mind. I think we can drive south and enter Yellowstone from the southwest corner. It's called Cascade Corner because it has so many waterfalls. It's also a remote part of Yellowstone, and I think it's unlikely we will see the mystery timer. Hopefully, we can work our way diagonally into the park and see more than if we cut straight across. It would be farther and take longer, but I think worth it. I don't want to come this far and not see the geyser basins."

"Also, you want to see what the waterfalls look like," said his brother.

"That as well. What does everyone think?"

All agreed that it sounded like a fine idea. The next question, How do they find their way in?

"That is where it might get a little tricky," said William, scratching a mosquito bite on the back of his hand. "I think we can count rivers and turn on the correct one…I think. Once we get on the right river going into the park, I believe it won't be too difficult. Paul, keep an eye on your compass. When you get a steady northeast reading, we need to leave the Madison and drive due south. Then it's a matter of counting rivers and turning up the correct one."

"Will do."

"Brother, you sure make it sound easy."

"Well, Bob, consider it false confidence."

Several hours later as they were flying between a corridor of trees, Paul spoke up, "William, we have been on a northwest heading for the last fifteen minutes. Is that long enough?"

"Well, in fifteen minutes, we should cover something over three miles. I think that's long enough. At the next opening to the south, take it."

A few minutes later, Paul said, "William, I see an opening in the trees just ahead."

"Take it!"

Paul eased the Timer through the opening, set the compass on dead south, and sped up. Almost immediately, he heeled the Timer hard left and yelled, "Look out below!"

William and Spear skidded across the deck, catching themselves on the railing. They were passing directly over an Indian encampment. Horses reared. Men, women, and children scattered. There were shouts of anger, people were running into and out of teepee's, and a small herd of horses ran toward a huge meadow off to the west. It was genuine, pure bedlam.

Recovering his senses, Paul went to maximum speed. Several arrows arched over the Timer, with one hitting the right side with a clang and bouncing off. In a minute, they were past the village, out of arrow range, and headed south as fast as the Timer would go. They were surprised the Indians didn't follow them. Regardless, the friends were thankful they did not.

"How about that!" exclaimed Bob. "I wonder who and what they think we are. Do you think our image will be drawn on a deer or buffalo skin one day?"

"I doubt it. We went through their camp and out of sight in a few seconds," answered his brother. "I don't think they could agree on what they saw or what we looked like."

Ellie slowly turned and looked around at the others and then started laughing. The others, including Spear, soon joined in.

Tears of laughter were streaming down Ellie's face as she asked, "Wonder who was more surprised, us or them?"

They began to pass through rolling country of large flower-covered meadows interspersed with small streams and forest patches. Paul kept the needle on due south, and the miles rolled by.

William was down below looking at maps. After a few minutes, he called the others to join him. Paul continued to drive but tried to tune an attentive ear to what was being said.

William spread out his map on the table and began explaining his plans. "I want group approval. We should be just west of the western boundary of Yellowstone. I think we should head due south until we hit the Falls River. We can camp there. That should be just south of the southwest corner of the park. I should say where the park will be. I'm guessing it to be no more than seventy to seventy-five miles from here. We ought to make it by dark, if not before."

He then opened a large map of modern-day Yellowstone National Park. "I think I can navigate us into the center of the park using the river system. It may not be easy, but if we can identify the correct rivers, I don't think we'll get lost, assuming we can overcome any obstacles we confront."

"You said the southwest corner was called Cascade Corner because of all the waterfalls?" asked Ellie. "Can we get over the falls?"

"Many may be too high for us to cross. It definitely remains to be seen," replied Bob. "I know we can get around some of them, but it may be a slow, tedious process. I just don't know."

"I bet you can figure it out," she said.

"Regardless, the banks may be open and not too high. Also, we may be able to force our way through trees if it becomes totally necessary," added William with a shrug.

Bob looked at William. "Let's hope it doesn't become necessary too many times."

They joined Paul on the top deck, lay down, and enjoyed the ride. Paul agreed wholeheartedly with the plans.

After several hours, William told Paul to angle slightly southeast and start counting rivers. "It should be the fourth one we come to if my calculations are correct. If not correct, we'll have to backtrack and try another one."

"I guess this is where the slow and tedious starts," joked Bob as he pulled and untied one of his brother's boot strings.

After several more hours, Paul pointed to the southeast, "Look over there." All the friends turned their heads to the left, and their eyes followed Paul's finger.

Bob laughed. "That's the Idaho side of the Tetons. Wow, you can see Grand in the center with that cloud wrapped around the peak. They still look the same, high, steep, and amazing."

"Will we get to see 1805 Jackson Hole?" asked Paul.

"We'll be a good deal north of the valley. We probably won't see it this trip, maybe another time. After Mr. Rockefeller bought his thirty-five thousand acres, much of it reverted to wilderness. I bet it doesn't look too different, except for paved roads and a few buildings," answered William.

"It shouldn't be too much farther to the Falls River now, Paul. It can't be more than a few miles ahead," said Bob.

Paul leaned forward and gave a long look ahead. "Actually, I think the fourth river is coming up, William."

They could see a narrow line of trees extending west from a thick forest just north of the massive, blocky shape of a mountain, which Bob said was Mt. Moran. Paul steered the Timer toward the tree line and said, "Let's start looking for a place to set up camp."

They found a small glade next to the river. Paul steered the Timer gently against the trees and settled it to the ground. They found that the limbs seemed to pop out over the Timer if it was set down correctly. This reduced the number of cut limbs necessary to conceal the Timer each night. It was just a little more labor-free concealment.

Bob, William, and Spear set out to get a load of the plentiful dried wood scattered around their campsite. Paul began shutting down the Timer for the night, and Ellie started digging through the food supplies. They found, in order to get a variety of meals, they had to go through the different bags and select from each. They had grouped too much of the same things together. They also decided to mark the contents of each bag in a more discernible way next time.

The wood gatherers returned with armloads of dried branches and dropped them into a pile. Spear knelt and made a small pile of dry needles. He then snapped off some slender branches and shaped them like a tepee over the needles. William noted this must have been the universal way of building campfires down through the ages.

Spear turned to Bob and said, "Fire."

Bob took a red butane lighter from his pocket, and he handed it to Spear. Spear spun the starter wheel with his thumb and smiled with delight when the flame leaped forth. He never seemed to tire of this small miracle that took place every night. He touched the fire to the needles, which immediately burst into flame. The fire quickly rose up through the framework of branches, and the kindling blackened and began to burn. Now he piled larger branches onto the fire, and it soon rose to a warming height.

Spear looked at the lighter with great reverence and then handed it back to Bob. Bob, seeing Spear's expression, stared at the lighter in his large palm. He looked at Spear and then back at the lighter. He leaned toward Spear, handing the lighter to him. "It's yours, Spear."

Spear looked at the lighter in his hand and up at Bob. With a quizzical look on his face, he said to Bob "It's yours, Spear?" as he patted his chest.

Bob reached over, placed his left hand on Spear's chest and his right on his opposite shoulder, and said, "Spear's."

"That was nice, Bob," said Ellie as she looked on. "He probably hasn't been given many things in life."

"Thanks, Ellie," said Bob as he thought, *Neither have you.*

Smiling broadly, Spear looked as if he had been given the contents of one of the treasure rooms back at their base. He rolled the lighter around in his hand and then placed it in a small deerskin pouch he wore around his neck. This was where he kept his most treasured possessions, including one of his gold nuggets.

CHAPTER 19

INTO YELLOWSTONE

PAUL SET A metal tripod over the fire. After a few minutes, he hung a large pot from it. The pot's base had been smoked black, defying all efforts to clean it. Ellie reached over the pot and poured in a large can of beef stew. It soon bubbled, giving off a delicious smell.

"Not too many cans of stew left. We're going to have to ration, improvise, or run out," she said.

"One time, William and I were down to a can of beef stew and one of pork and beans. We mixed the two, and they were wonderful," said Bob.

"And the fact that we were starving didn't hurt either," added his brother with a knowing look.

Bob laughed and looked at his brother. "We were definitely starving. It was like Dailey says, 'Keep them waiting long enough and they'll enjoy anything.'"

They all had coffee after supper. Spear enjoyed anything sweet and was sure to always put plenty of sugar in his, and tonight was no exception. After three spoonful's of sugar, Bob remarked, "With Spear, the old joke is true. He likes a little coffee with his sugar." With a puzzled look, Spear joined the others in laughter.

Each night, they worked with Spear to teach him English, and they were learning his language as fast as he was learning theirs. It was making for an interesting blend of both languages in all conversations. This was particularly true with Spear. His ten-word sentences would frequently be comprised of seven English words and three Crow ones. It could be confusing at times.

Spear had also been working on a bow and arrows, making a bow after finding juniper, which he said worked well. The bowstring was a tough, twisted nylon cord. His problem was arrows or, more specifically, arrowheads. He fletched shafts with bird feathers picked up along the rivers. He had not been able to find flint or any other materials to make into arrowheads.

Paul took notice of the problem and motioned Spear to sit beside him. Paul removed some wire cutters from his pocket and began cutting squares from the stew can he had just washed in the river. Putting two squares together for strength, he folded them over with pliers to make triangles. Each square had a smaller square projecting from the base. When done correctly, after two folds, these smaller squares extended a little beneath the arrowhead's triangle shape, making an effective base to attach to the shaft.

Spear touched the tip of a homemade arrowhead and smiled at Paul. The points were quite sharp. Working at a decidedly faster pace than his friend, he began fitting the arrowheads onto the shafts.

Paul turned to the others. "Spear has made arrows, and they are footed arrows."

Bob asked what everyone was thinking. "What is a footed arrow?"

Paul picked up one of Spear's arrows and assumed the attitude of a teacher. "That means it has been constructed from two different types of wood. You can see here at the top of the shaft where the two woods are joined together. The top wood is harder, so it won't break when the arrow strikes something. The rest of the shaft is a much softer wood. This works to keep the shaft lighter. It's obvious. Spear knows what he's doing."

Hearing his name, Spear looked up and nodded. The others laughed.

He quickly completed his first arrow. The arrowhead's base fit into a slot cut in the top of the shaft. The twine had been tightly wrapped around this base and down the shaft, making it quite sturdy.

Spear reached for his bow and the bowstring, attached the string to one end of the bow, and stood up. Placing the end with bowstring attached against his foot, he bent the bow and attached the other end. After giving the bow a test draw, which gave a pleasant twang, he took the finished arrow and fitted its notch onto the bowstring. Quickly surveying the clearing, he chose a target. In a quick, smooth motion, he drew the arrow to his cheek and, with his right eye, sighted down the shaft. Releasing the bowstring produced a sharp twang, and the arrow flew straight and true. In a split second, it quivered in the trunk of a nearby lodgepole pine.

The others clapped and cheered. He made it look so easy; it was obvious that years of practice were behind that shot. Spear looked both pleased and embarrassed.

Paul walked over to the tree and pulled out the arrow. Bringing it back to Spear, he remarked, "Its point bent a little, but not too bad." Paul handed Spear the arrow and patted him on the back. "Good shooting. Really good shooting!"

With a humble smile, Spear returned to fitting arrowheads on shafts with renewed enthusiasm. The others sat around the fire for a while, discussing Spear's shot and their plans for the next day. As there was a hint of rain in the air, one by one they climbed the Timer's ladder and crawled inside their sleeping bags. Soon, the only sound was the rain hitting the Timer and their light breathing.

Though it had rained during the night, the next morning dawned sunny and clear. The crew climbed out of the Timer to cool, sparkling air and the scent of evergreen.

Their usual breakfast of oatmeal was topped with a welcomed surprise. Spear had gotten up early and found some wild strawberries. While not as large as the modern variety, they were a tasty change. They had all grown tired of raisins and dried banana and apple flakes. The strawberries were a very welcome treat. They roundly praised Spear for his food-gathering abilities.

As he finished his last spoonful of oatmeal and strawberries, William spoke up, "We should find out today if we're on the right river. If we are, we'll hit the Bechler River and then the waterfalls. If we're on the correct water system, then we'll see if I can navigate us all the way into Yellowstone. I feel certain I can ultimately get us through the park. It's just that there are lots of mountains and other obstacles between us and the heart of Yellowstone. I guess we will answer that question one way or the other today."

The friends climbed to the upper deck and took their places. Paul easily and gently raised the Timer fifteen feet in the air, pulled out onto the center of the river, and headed upstream.

It was a beautiful morning for traveling. The weather was sunny with crispness in the air that hinted at the beginning of the end of the short Wyoming summer. They passed over small, bubbling rapids with the bottle green water making gurgling, splashing sounds and several times surprised moose feeding in river's shallows. They startled hundreds of ducks, geese, and cranes into flight. It seemed just a sensational day to be traveling up a backcountry river in a beautiful setting, heading toward one of the most famous places on earth.

They had been traveling for several hours when William pointed, "That may be the rapids just before Cave Falls."

Ahead, there was a series of six- to eight-foot rapids stretching across the river. "The first time Bob and I drove here to see Cave Falls, we thought that was it. Were we ever disappointed! We were about to drive away when I walked around that bend in the river."

Ellie leaned toward William. "Cave Falls? That seems like a funny name for a waterfall. Where does it get its name?"

"There is a large cave near the falls that gives it that name. We should be able to see it to the left of the falls when we get there."

"Can we stop and look at it?" she asked.

"Sure."

"William, I think we've got company," said his brother in a calm but deadly serious voice.

The others turned and followed Bob's gaze down the river. The black timer rounded a bend several hundred yards back and came on fast. They saw its crew scrambling out of the conning tower, making frenzied gestures toward them. There were several flashes then the whine of bullets passing overhead. The rapids and falls almost drowned out the gunshots.

"Everyone, below!" shouted William, waving his arm toward the hatch. "Hurry now, they're not too far behind us."

"Nope, I'm staying up here with you," Paul said very matter-of-factly.

Bob followed with a quick "Me, too, William!"

Grasping his younger brother by the arm, William said, "Bob, you're too big a target. Please go below right now."

"Okay, William, if you say so," and he reluctantly climbed down the ladder to join Ellie and Spear.

William said, "Paul, keep your head as low as possible and let's see if we can figure something out."

"Okay. Until we decide on a plan, I'm heading upriver." They flew over the humble rapids, rounding the river bend.

"Wow!" exclaimed Paul. "Now that's a waterfall!"

William eyed the spectacular falls in front of him. "At least we know we're on the right river," he said, irony in his voice.

A waterfall over twenty feet high roared in front of them and extending bank to bank, two hundred and fifty feet across. Tall trees lined the banks, and they saw no place to run. They were trapped.

Paul stopped a hundred feet short of the falls and looked at William. "What do we do now?"

"I should have realized Cave Falls would have been a little higher in 1805 and then worn down some by our time. When I saw it before, the falls weren't this high. Well, it seems like we don't have many options. There are two, but I really don't like either. We can turn downstream and try to get by them. Or…we can surrender. Neither appeals to me very much."

"Me either," Paul replied, looking determined.

They looked behind them and saw the other timer entering the bend in the river. Even over the fall's thunder, they could hear shouts and laughter as the other crew realized they were about to capture their foes.

William turned to Paul. "Okay, option three. Give it everything we've got and head for the falls."

CHAPTER 20

ESCAPE 2?

"Okay, William, you know I'll do what you say, but aren't we going to crash into the falls?"

"Maybe, but maybe not. I don't think we have much choice but to try. We're captured for sure if we stay around here. I don't like to think what would happen if they got their hands on Bob."

"Well, you're right about that. I say let's go for it!"

Having decided there were no other means of escape, they were now committed to something they weren't sure would work. Paul accelerated the Timer to maximum speed over the last fifty yards to Cave Falls. William quickly leaned down and told the others below to close the hatch and hold on.

"Paul, keep a tight grip on that wheel," William said, reaching behind and getting a firm grip on the railing.

The Timer got there in a few seconds as the roaring, plunging Cave Falls soared above them. The bottom of the Timer hit the falls, and for several seconds, water poured over the railing. They began to slowly tilt back as Paul and William struggled to hold on. As the Timer turned nearly vertical, it seemed on the verge of falling backward to the river below. Suddenly, the front dipped, and the Timer seemed to skip up and over the fall's edge. It was like a rock skipping across the surface of a lake. As the rear passed the over the lip of the falls, the Timer immediately rose to its customary fifteen feet and continued up the river. Paul swung the Timer first one way then the other to avoid giving a steady target to their pursuers.

"Wow, how about that for a thrill?" yelled Paul.

"How about that for a relief?" William said as he wiped water from his eyes.

Less than a hundred yards behind them, they heard shouts of dismay and anger and saw flashes from several random shots, but Paul had lowered the Timer to only a few feet off the water. The angle was now bad for accurate shooting, and the bullets passed well over their heads. They were quickly moving out of range.

Looking back, William could see a huge young man waving his fists at them and unquestionably hurling curses their way. He was sure to be saying what he would do when he caught them.

Then the top hatch opened, and Bob climbed out onto the deck. "Hey, that's my buddy! That's the guy I rescued Spear from."

William watched as his brother stood on the top step of the ladder and waved back at the other timer. His large adversary spotted him and renewed his fist shaking and screaming. Seeing this, Bob threw back his head laughing and waved again. This caused even more emphatic fist waving and curse screaming, and Bob muttered, "This is really great! Just look at that big goof."

William shook his head at Paul. "There is nobody like my brother. There is absolutely no one that scares him."

Bob suddenly stood up on his tiptoes and shielded his eyes. "William, I think they're going to try to get over the falls as well."

As they watched, the sinister black timer appeared to speed up and head directly at Cave Falls. A few seconds later, it hit the falling water, and its rounded front rose high in the air.

"They may make it," said William with some alarm in his voice.

"No! Look, I don't think so," replied Paul.

The other timer had climbed almost half its length trying to clear over the waterfall. Its front seemed to almost tip over onto the river above, but then it slowly slid backward below the lip of the falls and turning on its right side. With now only the top of the conning tower showing, the white, foamy water poured over the enemy timer, driving it down toward the river below and out of sight.

Paul clapped William on the shoulder. "Wow, did you see that?"

The black timer emerged into view from beneath the falls as it was rapidly carried downstream like a chip of wood. Its front end dipped low in the water, but it remained afloat. It was then swept out of sight around the bend and down the river.

"How did we make it over the top and they didn't?" Paul asked, turning toward William.

"I think the principle is about the same as skimming a flat stone or a length of pipe across a lake. One is designed for skipping and one isn't," said William, grinning.

"They are going to have fun going over those rapids," said Paul.

"Right, and how about the drop that's around the bend? It's going to take them a while to get things sorted out," added Bob, bemused.

"Don't count them out yet," said William. "That's twice their shape has worked against them and saved us. It may be our turn next time."

William stepped forward, putting a hand on Paul's arm. "Paul, take the next river to the left. That will be the Bechler River."

Bob threw a large arm around his brother's shoulder. "Now is where we get creative. Let's see if we can find a way to Yellowstone's interior from Cascade Corner in a time machine."

"Right. It will be interesting."

A few minutes later, Paul asked, "William, what do I do here?"

William looked up to see a fork in the river a hundred yards ahead. "Stay on the main channel Paul. That's Boundary Creek to the left."

Bob leaned against his brother. "Let me guess. I bet Boundary Creek gets its name because it follows the western boundary of Yellowstone?"

"I bet you're correct. Now don't get me confused. I'm trying to keep all these lefts and rights straight in my head."

"Exactly where are you getting all these lefts and rights?" asked Bob.

William took a folded map from his back pocket. "It's the official map and guide to Yellowstone. It's all here. I got it on our last trip to the park.

"The time we hiked into Union Falls and you were so scared of running into that mother grizzly and her two cubs on the way out?"

"Yes, that time, and I had good reason to be concerned. Remember, we had seen them the day before only a few miles away. I didn't want to run into that bear family away from our truck. And to answer your first question, I've memorized most of this map in case I lose it or it gets wet and falls into pieces."

"Memorized it, huh? Okay, what's coming up?"

Looking up the river, William closed his eyes for a few seconds and then, hands on hips, answered, "About five miles past Boundary is Ouzel Creek, but we stay on the Bechler."

"Why?" both Paul and Bob asked at the same time.

"Ouzel Falls is over two hundred feet high. That tells me steep terrain. In the Timer, steep terrain is not our friend."

"Okay, no waterfalls on the Bechler?" said Bob with a chuckle.

"Colonnade Falls is one hundred feet high but two-tiered. One tier is sixty-something feet, and the other tier is thirty-something feet. The land must go up more gradually. We may be able to climb up the two levels."

"Okay, okay, I give up. Only my brother and his photographic memory could remember all this stuff."

From behind them, Ellie said, "We may still need some open meadows regardless of what route we take. I also memorized it."

"Okay, two geniuses, I double give up. Is it two genius or two geniuses?"

Patting him on the head, Ellie said, "You were correct, it is two geniuses although I think that is overstating it quite a bit."

"Doesn't matter, we've got to get through no matter what we are confronted with," said William. "We are going into the interior between the Madison and Pitchstone Plateaus. That has got be the easiest way to go even if it's not easy. I want us to get past these waterfalls and well into the interior before the other timer dries out and follows us."

Ellie nodded and agreed. "Looking at the map, William is right. This is rough country we're trying to move through, but I think he's chosen the best route. It's got to be easier moving over water most of the time than trying to fly cross country."

Several miles later, having stayed on the Bechler River, they came to the impressive Colonnade Falls. The river flowed over a sheer drop with the tumbling water making a white circle in the pool below.

"Wow, that is a beautiful waterfall," said Ellie, shielding her eyes from the sun. "The two tiers look almost identical, only the lower one is a bit higher."

"The lower one is higher?" said Bob as he sat with an index finger pressed against the side of his head. "Actually, I do understand."

Pointing to the left side, Paul said, "That looks more open. I wonder if we can get over the bank."

Studying the left bank, William said, "Let's see if we can ease up that bank. Paul, do you see where that spring is flowing into the river? Let's try there."

Paul slowly flew to a low spot in the bank. The front of their craft was almost touching the volcanic rock when it rose slowly in the air. Paul now urged the Timer over the edge of the bank and between two very large lodgepole pines. They then cruised over a tangle of underbrush and downed trees. This area appeared to flood during the big spring snowmelt. As they moved ahead cautiously, the path cleared. It was still dotted with trees, but they were spaced in groups that were set well-apart.

"Straight forward, Paul, then we can cross over the river just below the second falls. That side looks more open than this side," directed William.

The second falls was only half the size of the lower falls. As the obsidian rocks on the right side sloped up at an easy angle, this part would not be a problem. Paul nodded his head and steered for the upper falls.

William walked to the front and studied the land's configuration. "Paul, it looked easy a minute ago, but it doesn't look that easy now. Let's switch directions back and forth and slowly work our way up. Go as far as you can in one direction, then go the other way. Treat it like switchbacks on a mountainside."

William's plan worked. Only at the steepest part, near the top, was there a question whether they could make it. Make it they did. They topped the ridge fifty yards to the right of where the river plunged down the falls. Paul pulled above the middle of the river and flew upstream.

They had only gone a short distance when they ran into yet another waterfall. "And that is Iris Falls," said William, a hint of dejection in his voice.

"Are we going to keep running into waterfalls as frequently as this? This could get old fast," Ellie said.

"No, thank goodness! They do thin out a bit before picking back up. Right now, we need to figure out how to get around Iris. One thing at a time."

Paul then flew the Timer across the river where they could get a good look at both sides. The slopes were not too steep, but they were thick with trees.

"Paul, set the Timer down on the north side. Bob and I can get down and look for a way through all these trees."

Paul dropped the Timer as gently as a butterfly in a small clearing surrounded on three sides by tall, mature trees. Bob and William climbed up from below, each with a dark pistol swinging from his hip. Bob, again, said it was better to have it and not need it than to need it and not have it.

"Wait a minute, William," said Bob. "Let's make sure we're loaded up." The two brothers checked their weapons, and they were both loaded.

They climbed down the ladder and pushed their way through the trees, scaring a young fox in the process. The two had not gone far when the forest opened slightly and a burned-over area of lodgepole pines appeared. Walking to the edge of the forest, the boys looked out over a wide swath of burned trees standing like white columns, totally devoid of leaves, some standing and many lying jumbled at all angles on the ground.

"I've got an idea, William. How far is it back through the forest to the Timer?"

"Not far, probably fifty feet."

Looking back through the trees, Bob asked, "How many big trees?"

"I don't know, probably six, eight, no more than ten."

Bob smiled. "I think we can chop down six, eight, or ten trees in a few hours. They are not that big. I hate to do it, but we're really kind of in a bind right now."

"You're probably right, and I bet Paul can push through some of the smaller ones. I do see a problem though. What do we do when we get to this point? Look at all these dead trees blocking our way."

"Well, let me try something. I think I can take that worry off your mind."

Bob walked over to one of the dead lodgepole pines standing near the edge of the living forest. He put his shoulder against the trunk, gave it a shove, and the tree swayed out and then back. He then timed as the tree swayed out again and gave it a harder push. Timing the sway one more time, as it went out again, Bob pushed with all his might. This time, the tree toppled, and the roots pulled up a large ball of dirt. The trunk came crashing down on a pile of trees that had previously fallen. The fallen trees lay folded together like pickup sticks.

Wiping soot off his shoulder, Bob turned to his brother, smiling. "Well, how about that?"

"How did you know it would do that?" William asked with a look of astonishment on his face.

"Remember that summer I volunteered with the Forest Service in the Teton Wilderness? I learned they may look solid, but the wind blows them over all the time. I saw my ranger friend, Nick, push several down when they were hanging dangerously over our trail clearing. He didn't want someone getting hurt or killed."

"And he was strong?"

"Yes, he was very strong."

"But he wasn't as strong as you?"

"Right, he was very strong but not as strong as me."

"I bet Paul can push through these dead trees like nothing," William said over his shoulder as he started walking back to the Timer.

He returned in a few minutes with two single-bit axes. For the next several hours, they chopped at the larger trees that stood in their way. Bob was particularly good as he hit with tremendous force, large chips flying. During one of the breaks, William reached in a back pocket and brought out a large file. Using this file, he put a fine edge back on each axe.

"Don't let the edge get in the dirt," Bob said. "That's something else I learned with the Forest Service. It dulls the blade."

They had soon laid down all the larger trees. As best they could tell, there were mostly only younger, smaller trees blocking the Timers way to the burned over area.

Putting canvas covers over the heads of their axes, they remounted the Timer. Paul began to ease his way through the trees along the path they had just chopped. After pushing aside some of the standing but smaller trees, they were able to squeeze between the larger trees still standing. Paul drove them between the last two erect trees with inches to spare. Finally, they flew out over the burn.

"Take it easy, Paul. The trees may be dead, but they are still hard. You should be able to push them over if necessary. We just don't want to hit them going too fast," instructed Bob.

Following Bob's instructions, Paul worked his way slowly, but carefully, through the burned trees. He would ease up against a tree trunk and gently accelerate. With only two exceptions, the trees slowly toppled over. Twice, Paul found it necessary to improvise a little. He steered around one of the more stubborn trees and increased to maximum power to shove the other one aside. After two hours zigzagging through the burn, they had climbed the ridge. Paul pulled up to the Bechler River just above Iris Falls. This was at least one waterfall they didn't have to worry about. They pulled out over the river and continued their journey into the heart of Yellowstone.

CHAPTER 21

TREASURE ISLAND

THE GROUP SETTLED back on the Timer's deck, grateful and glad the tree cutting and pushing were finished…at least for the time being. Paul sat in the driver's seat, and the others leaned back against the railing.

"We need a swim after all that hard, hot, sweaty work," offered Bob. "William, can you find a nice spot near the river to set up camp? I'm thinking of one with a beach, an umbrella, and diving board."

"William, which way do we go up ahead?" Paul asked, seeing that the river seemed to divide.

William looked upstream. "If I'm not mistaken, I believe we are coming up on Treasure Island, Paul. That's not a fork. That's an island."

"Did you say Treasure Island?" asked Paul, skeptically.

"I did."

"Is treasure there? Maybe there's a nice pirate's chest full of gold doubloons," Ellie said facetiously.

"Actually, an early explorer said it reminded him of the island in the book by Robert Louis Stevenson."

Bob took off his boots. "Well, it is getting to be late in the afternoon, and it does look like a good place to spend the night. I bet there's also a good place to have a swim."

William placed a hand on Paul's shoulder. "Paul, see if you can find a good place to put down. Preferably, one with a nice beach for my brother."

Circling the small, forested island, Paul agreed to do his best. In a minute, he located a small meadow on the south side. William said it would do fine despite no diving board. The others agreed immediately.

It turned out to be better than fine; it turned out to be perfect. This was especially true for Bob, who pronounced it ideal.

The meadow was ringed by several large, downed trees that would make perfect seats around a fire. It was also near a group of springs flowing out of the canyon wall. Together, they formed small waterfalls flowing down into the Bechler. All in all, regardless of no diving board or beach, it looked to be a great place for a swim.

The friends decided it would be safe for them to build a fire that night. There would be clothes that needed drying. They had little food that was better cold than cooked, and the nights were getting cooler. It seemed unlikely the other timer could make it this far today after its travails at Cave Falls. It was also doubtful they could easily travel in this rough, hilly country after dark. Paul also pointed out the numerous streams and rivers they would pass. With all the choices available, if the other timer came their way, they would have to be indeed unlucky.

Nodding, Bob agreed. "I wonder if they'll have problems getting their timer functional? That dunking in the river couldn't have been good for it. I don't know how something similar would affect us, but it couldn't possibly be good."

"You're probably right, Bob, but let's stay on our toes anyway. We can't count on a little water getting in their gas tank to stop these guys. I'm betting they got buttoned up before that water came over the top of their timer anyway. I'm thinking they may not have any water in their craft. I think they kind of got turned upside down and lost their lift, and floating with one end down may not be the best way to get it back."

After Spear built fire, Ellie emerged from the Timer in a dark blue, single-piece bathing suit. The guys then went below and returned shirtless in nylon hiking shorts.

Bob took a running start and leaped out as far into the water as he could. The others used the toe-in-the-water approach at first but soon joined him, Bob having hastened them by splashing cold water on them as they stood on the bank.

They took turns going to the small waterfalls and soaping up. Ellie said she had never needed to wash her hair as much as she did that day. There was a good supply of biodegradable soap, and they had used very little of it. They stood near the bank, soaped up, and then stood under one of the waterfalls. The water was clean but very cold. They joked how nice one of Yellowstone's fabled hot springs would have been today.

The river also had various eddies and pools perfectly suited for bathing. Bob took Spear along the bank to one of the pools where he playfully pushed him in. Bob had made sure it wasn't deep as Spear couldn't swim. Bob jumped in after him and retrieved a bottle of soap he had placed on the bank. He squirted some in his hand and did the same with Spear. He then showed him how to wash his hair by demonstrating on himself. Bob's thick hair was soon a blob of white soap suds. Motioning Spear to follow, he led him to a nearby waterfall. Ducking his head under the falling water, Bob showed Spear how it made the soap disappear. Spear followed suit and was obviously delighted with the new experience. He held out his hand to Bob for more soap and repeated the process. The third was the final time.

As each of them finished, they returned to huddle by the restoked fire. Everyone stretched out hands and feet as close to the fire as possible. This day had started off bad but had finished with a flourish. They all felt safe, clean, and hungry.

Ellie climbed inside the Timer and emerged in a few minutes wearing fresh clothes. The boys quickly followed suit. Bob pointed out that he had been wearing the same clothes for two weeks. This was followed by a chorus of "We know!"

After adding more wood to the fire, William ladled hot, bubbling stew to the crew. Soon quietness prevailed as they ate. After they finished, they sat around talking about their day's adventures. They all made sure to draw Spear into the conversation. His English continued to improve. They had found that drawing him into frequent conversations accelerated the learning curve. Ellie was working hard with him, and progress was clear. After eating, they all enjoyed a cup of tea or coffee. As usual, Spear had sweetened his coffee with multiple spoons full of sugar.

William sat on a log with his legs outstretched out and crossed at the ankles. "We've been very remiss in taking only the occasional photos. When we get to the park's interior, we need to take more because we need to better document what we see. Who knows? These pictures may someday have historical significance."

"Who would we show them to?" asked Ellie, curious.

"I don't know, but if we don't take them, I bet we'll regret it one day."

Rubbing her hands together against the cool air, Ellie said, "I agree. We will probably want to look at them ourselves. Also, there may be someone we want to show them to, like a favorite professor."

"Yeah, a favorite professor that can keep his mouth shut," responded Bob, poking the fire with a long stick.

"Okay, who wants to take stills, and who wants to record?" continued William.

"I like flying the Timer, or I would be glad to do either," said Paul.

Bob clapped Paul on the back. "You're right, Paul, you are the best driver. I'll be glad to do either."

Ellie leaned back against a large rock. "Okay, let me record. I have always been a frustrated director. But remember this…don't look at the camera, don't pose, and try to act naturally."

Bob smiled. "Have we created a monster? Oh well, suits me. I'll do the stills. I don't want to get in the way of Ms. Scorsese here."

Smiling, William said, "Why don't we all do the stills? Bob can be in charge, but if anyone has a scene they want to take, get the camera from Bob. How did we manage to bring only one camera? Whatever you do, don't drop it. There is no backup!"

Suddenly, Spear blurted out, "Good, very good!"

The others looked at him as he ran his index finger around the coffee cup and popped it into his mouth. The friends laughed, clapping their hands and congratulating him for using the words correctly.

As bedtime approached, Bob walked to the river and returned with a pot of water, using it to douse the fire. They all climbed into their sleeping bags for a well-earned night's rest.

The next morning dawned cool, bright, and clear with only a few clouds scuttling across the vivid blue sky. They spread out the prior night's ashes. Spear leaned over the fire ring they constructed the day before, carefully placing of driftwood the others had just collected and started the morning fire. Soon, they had coffee heating and oatmeal cooking. Opening a new bag of trail mix to add to the oatmeal, they discovered it had M&Ms in it. Almost everyone was delighted with this unexpected treat.

Paul looked skeptically at the M&Ms. "I don't know about these in oatmeal." He was proven wrong as they had a new flavor to add to their otherwise monotonous meal.

Ellie reached over and picked out two of the red ones. She handed one to Spear and put the other one in her mouth.

Spear rolled it around in his fingers and then placed it on his tongue. "Good!" he said with a big smile.

The others smiled and voiced their appreciation of his burgeoning understanding of English even though most of it seemed to revolve around the usage of the word "good."

Spear smiled and said, "Very, very good, sweet very!" This caused polite clapping and enthusiastic cheering. At least he had even added the word "sweet" to his vocabulary.

The bowls were soon scraped clean and washed in the river. Bob said his plate was almost clean to not need washing. Everyone, including Paul, wished they had more M&Ms for their next meal.

Bob returned from the river with water to douse their fire. They scattered fire ring stones, smoothed dirt over the ashes, and loaded their cooking equipment on the Timer. As the crew arranged themselves on the deck, Paul lifted them off the island and out over the river. Treasure Island was soon far behind.

After a while, they flew over a beautiful stretch of white water. William said one day it would be named Washboard Cascade. The water practically danced, pitched, and roiled over the rocks in a rollicking fashion. Farther ahead, the water smoothed out to a glassy, flat surface, and Bob asked William what their next landmark would be.

"We are looking for Little's Fork of the Bechler River. We'll pass several possibilities, but I think you and I can recognize the correct one. If you'll remember, we have hiked in the area several times."

It was not long before William pointed ahead and said, "I think that's the Gregg Fork on the left and Little's Fork on the right."

Bob pointed to Little's Fork and asked, "William, what's the name of that waterfall, and are we going to have to climb it?"

"It probably is classified as a cascade. I think that would be Littlesmouth Cascade."

Bob nodded his head. "I bet you're right. That makes sense, it's at the mouth of Little's Fork."

"Looks like a waterfall to me, so what's the difference?" asked Paul, looking quizzical.

"Usually, a cascade is a series of waterfalls and not as steep," answered William.

Sitting back in his seat, Paul asked, "Do you think the Timer will climb it?"

After studying the cascade for a minute, William answered, "I think so. Stay on the right side of the rock that juts out of the water. I think that looks like the more gradual grade. and it's only a climb of forty-five feet."

Paul steered the Timer to the right side of Littlesmouth Cascade and eased forward. The Timer cantered back slightly with the rear portion touching the foamy water. However, in a few seconds, it rose above the water, and Paul slowly drove it to the top.

"That was easy," said Paul with a look of surprise on his face.

"Only two more climbs to go, and we should drop over the rim of the caldera and into the center of Yellowstone," William happily noted.

"Caldera, what's a caldera?" asked Paul, looking puzzled.

"Short definition or long definition?" inquired Bob.

"The short definition will be fine."

Putting on his most studious look, Bob answered, "A caldera is the mouth of a volcano. When Yellowstone had an eruption 650,000 years ago, it emptied a huge magma chamber, and the surrounding country then collapsed into it. In the years since, it has partially filled in. You can still see the rim if you know what you're looking for."

"Bob's right, Paul," said William. "This caldera is so big people didn't realize they were looking at a volcano."

"How big is it?"

"It's roughly forty-five miles by thirty-four miles. They discovered what it was through satellite photos."

"Gosh, that is big!" Ellie said amazed.

"Yes, it's big," replied William. "We're closing in on it with only two obstacles to go. Our next hurdle is Tempe Falls. I think it's very much like what we just climbed. There is a cave near the falls, and the word Tempe means 'cave' in Shoshone."

Shaking his head, Bob spoke up, "William, your memory is absolutely amazing. No wonder you don't have to study."

Soon, they approached another glistening cascade with a rock cliff shouldering its right side.

After studying the cascade, Bob expressed his opinion of cascades. "Cascades look like shallow white water tilted up on one end. Tempe Falls doesn't look like it won't be hard to climb at all."

William smiled. "As scary as it is to say, what you said does make sense. The cascade you're looking at is just the first of four. It's the second one I'm most concerned about. It's not the highest, but it's the steepest."

"William, how do you know so much about these waterfalls and cascades?" questioned Paul.

"I read *To the Guide Yellowstone Waterfalls and Their Discovery*."

"There's a book on waterfalls in Yellowstone?" asked Paul, a perplexed look on his face.

"It's the Bible on waterfalls in Yellowstone."

Paul drove the Timer easily up the first and then on to the troubling second cascade. They were relieved to see the bottom half was a true drop of only ten feet.

"Boy, do I feel better! I was worried it might be a twenty-foot drop like Cave Falls. I hated the thought of getting out the axes," exclaimed William, looking relieved.

They passed over the first drop with five feet to spare and sprang over the second, again, with five feet to spare. Paul easily flew over the next three cascades. Each cascade was different and almost exotic in its own special way.

To everyone's relief, there was now only one potential obstruction between them and Yellowstone's interior. They agreed the last few days had been interesting, also agreed they were tired of the constant worry created by waterfalls and the irregular topography. The last feature they faced was Douglas Knob Falls. Little's Fork wound around in graceful curves and then came to the falls. It was twenty-five feet high but tiered so that the Timer climbed it easily. William pointed off to the east at Douglas Knob, namesake of the falls and 8,534 feet high.

"I've got to ask," interjected Ellie, "where did Douglas Knob get its name?"

"Joseph Douglas was a park ranger. He also was the park's chief buffalo keeper in the 1920s," replied William.

"Buffalo keeper? Oh, never mind," Ellie laughingly replied.

William also laughed and turned to Paul, "Take a course slightly west of due north." He informed the others this would take them to the vicinity of the Firehole River. The land began to open as they dropped into the caldera of the future Yellowstone National Park for the first time. They could see millions of trees for miles and miles. Scattered through the scenery were the occasional white smoke plumes. William said these would most likely be hot spots where steam vented through the surface. He said they were much easier to see in the winter when the steam hit the freezing air. Bob pointed out there would be an entry fee to enter Yellowstone National Park in sixty-seven years. The Firehole River they sought was to be their highway into the central part of the park.

"William, you told us what a caldera is now. Tell us a little about Yellowstone. It's unique in the world, isn't it?" asked Ellie.

William propped his chin in the palm of his left hand and began his recitation. "First, Yellowstone is unique in the world. It has ten thousand geothermal features including 60 percent of the geysers in the world. Beneath Yellowstone is a huge magma chamber. This magma lies very close to the surface, only about six miles. I can't remember exactly, but I think it's something like twenty-five miles by fifty miles in size. The heat from the magma is the primary reason for the hundreds of geysers and other geothermal features. I mentioned how big the caldera was after Yellowstone's last explosion. It was also thousands of feet deep. It scattered debris as far as Nebraska and created gigantic ash flows. The prevailing thought is that it will explode again one day."

"Well, we know it wasn't today," said Bob.

"Bro, you're right. It for sure wasn't today. I hadn't thought about that."

"It was a huge volcano," said Ellie, a touch of awe in her voice.

"That's about it. It was a super volcano," answered William.

The land dropped away in front of them as far as they could see. It consisted of forested areas and flower-streaked meadows. The forest fires had not reached this part of the park, and the trees were tall and mature. Paul drove the Timer down the mountainside and on a northwest heading as directed by William. The traveling was easy with very few places of thick growth. Even the stretches of thicker growth were not difficult, and Paul was able to pick his way through each thicket with ease. After several hours, Ellie pointed at a line of trees and said that it might be the Firehole River.

She was right. Paul eased the Timer between some trees, and a river stretched before them, flowing away to the north. Paul drove the craft down a low bank and out above the water. He settled the Timer over the river's center, set the height at fifteen feet, and headed north.

"This should be the Firehole, but we really need to look for some landmarks to be sure," said William as he looked carefully over his map.

"What kind of landmarks? Roads, ranger stations, and picnic areas?" inquired his brother with a smirk.

"Well, if you see any of those, I would sure be interested. Just look for any distinguishing place or thing. Anything that might show up on our map would be good. We can then use it to pinpoint our position."

A short while later, the crew heard a bubbling sound, closely followed by a whooshing noise. It seemed to come from the west side of the Firehole. William suggested they investigate. They hoped this might be one of those landmarks they were looking for. Paul soon found a gradual slope on the west bank. He flew the Timer up and over it, flying in the direction of the strange sounds.

The group hugged the front rail, manning a lookout in the westerly direction in which they were going. They rounded a small line of trees, and there, in front of them, was a very strange sight.

William smiled. "After seeing this, I think we're on the right river for sure."

Before them stood an eight-foot high, glistening cone of silver and pink geyserite still dripping water that ran across the ground in small rivulets.

"What in the world is that?" asked Paul, looking astonished.

"It looks different and is not as big as I remember, but I think that's Lone Star Geyser. It would have done a fair amount of growing between now and when I last saw it."

"Why is it called Lone Star Geyser?" asked Ellie with a giggle.

"Okay," said William. "Look around for the reason." He waited a few seconds then said, "Do you see any other geysers? Lone Star sits by itself with no others nearby. So for that reason, someone named it Lone Star Geyser."

"I presume you know we're on the right river because you think you recognize this as Lone Star Geyser. I guess that means Lone Star Geyser is on the Firehole River? Whew, that was a mouthful!" exclaimed Ellie as she hugged her arms across her chest.

"Not on but near the Firehole. I do believe this is Lone Star Geyser even though it's probably four or five feet shorter. A lot can happen in a couple of hundred years. The color, the setting, it just feels right," replied William as he surveyed the surrounding area.

"Look over there," said Bob in a low voice.

Turning to their left, the others watched as a herd of elk walked slowly out of the forest. Led by several huge bulls, their antlers were shaggy with tattered bits of velvet dangling down from the tines. The herd paid no attention to the Timer or crew and continued past Lone Star Geyser, disappearing into the forest and heading in the direction of the river.

"Well, if my brother is correct and that's Lone Star Geyser, we aren't far from Kepler Cascades. I have a feeling it's going to be much more fun going down cascades than what we've been doing."

"I agree with Bob. Paul, get us back to the river and let's get going. I can't wait to get into the interior and see what it looks like."

Paul got them back to the river and again headed north. They had traveled only several hundred yards when they rounded a bend and were directly over the elk herd. Elk reared and scattered in every direction with a mad splashing of water and pounding of hooves.

"Wow, I didn't mean to do that!" stammered Paul apologetically.

Chuckling, Bob patted his friend on the head. "No harm done, you couldn't have known they were waiting here to scare us."

"They may have scared you, boys, but they didn't scare me in the least," said Ellie with a superior look on her face.

"Sorry," said Bob. "I meant to say scared us boys."

"Better!" she replied.

CHAPTER 22

INTO THE HEART
OF THE PARK

PAUL KEPT THE Timer in the middle of the Firehole, traveling at the usual ten to fifteen miles per hour. Within an hour, they heard a distance roaring sound from up ahead. It almost sounded like continuous thunder.

"William, what is making that noise?"

"I'm betting that's Kepler Cascades we hear," said William, gazing yet again at his map.

Clapping his hands, Bob shouted, "This should be fun! I don't think anyone else has ever run these cascades like we can. Nobody else can go as low over this cascade without being thrown around by the water."

Sure enough, soon the cascades came into view, and Paul stopped the Timer so everyone could get a good, long look down the chute. Kepler Cascades dropped off down the ravine in three tiers; the last tier appeared the highest with the biggest drop. It was a maelstrom of white, churning water flowing like creamy milk from one tier to the next.

Everyone but Paul crawled to the front of the Timer and hung over the railing to get a better look. Spear's face sparkled with anticipation. The others' excitement was heightened by how amazed Spear was. Obviously, none had ever dreamed of doing such a thing as this, and neither had he.

"Let her rip, Paul!" yelled Bob as he tossed his cap below and got a death grip on the railing.

William looked around at the others. "Everyone, hold on tight. If you do fall in, lean back and go feet first. We'll pick you up at the first still water. Ellie, make sure Spear understands what I just said. Bob, make sure the hatch is shut tight. We don't want any water pouring down below."

Ellie quickly whispered in Spear's ear, and Bob locked the hatch. William nodded at Paul and said, "Let her rip, Paul!" Everyone laughed and held on. The fun was about to begin!

Paul flew smoothly over the edge of the first falls, and the Timer and crew fell away. Yells and cheers rang out as the Timer dropped and then abruptly stopped several feet above the water. The falls came pouring over the Timer and pouring over them. This brought on more cheers as it was something they had not anticipated. The Timer immediately rose to five feet above the boiling, plunging stream. Paul drove them out of the deluge of water and toward the next drop. He began skating the Timer down a river that had many more drops and plenty of the wet spray. They were all soaked to the skin but having a wonderful time. Paul discovered that the faster he drove over the edges, the less the Timer dipped in the front end. It also kept them clear of the water flow over the drop. He drove slowly over the flatter sections but ever faster over the drops. He soon had reduced almost all the dipping and swaying to nothing as they flew down the canyon and down Kepler Cascades.

"This is really cool!" Bob shouted to the others over the roar of the water. "It's like running white water without being in the water. I don't know anything other than the Timer that could give you this effect."

After dropping over a hundred feet from the top of the cascade to the bottom, they came to smooth, fast-running water that still flowed downstream at a rapid pace. Through the undergrowth on the bank, they could see more gaps between the trees, with fewer thickets and more spread out, open spaces. Much of the land was treeless, and they could see buffalo grazing in numerous places. Looking ahead, they got their first glimpse of the famous Upper Geyser Basin.

"I've always wondered how the Upper Geyser Basin could be south of the Lower Geyser Basin," speculated Bob as he shook water from his shaggy hair.

As the friends crowded to the railing to get a better view, they looked at one another and began laughing. Water poured from their clothes, hair, and down their faces. Paul told the others they looked like drowned rats, and they replied in kind. Spear asked Ellie what drowned rats meant, and that set off another wave of laughter when she tried to explain.

William rose cautiously to his feet, peering over the bushes to the right. "Paul, let's go in that direction. I see some trees that should make a good place to camp tonight. You did a great job of driving us down Kepler. That was pretty amazing."

Everyone turned their heads and followed William's gaze as he leaned against the top of the railing. They could see a grove of trees and, behind it, a large white area with steam rising from its center.

Paul drove the Timer through the small stand of trees, and they entered Yellowstone's Upper Geyser Basin. The land flattened out, and clouds of smoke rose from numerous, barren, and treeless areas scattered across the valley.

Bob spoke up, "You'll soon understand why William and I think this is such a special place. In approximately one square mile, there are around one hundred and fifty geysers. There's no other place on earth where there are so many geysers in such a small area. Like so much about Yellowstone, you can only see it here."

Paul now flew the Timer into the grove and lowered it to the ground. Bob and William climbed down the ladder, and the others began to toss gear to them. They started setting up camp and began supper preparations.

They had been there only a few minutes when William stood. He walked a few steps, bent with hands on his knees, and looked across the valley. "That, guys, I believe is Old Faithful." He pointed to a low mound of bleached earth several hundred yards away.

As the friends watched, they saw several splashes of water, and steam began to rise from the mound. There was a geothermal feature of some kind over there.

Ellie yelled "I'm getting closer!" and ran out of the trees. The others followed hot on her heels. They stopped fifty feet short of the geyser and watched as things began to happen.

Now water flowed out of the geyser's mouth and across the ground. In fits and starts water bounded upward, growing in intensity as more and more water and steam emitted from the mouth.

Suddenly, there was a burst of water forty to fifty feet high. Everyone shielded their eyes as each subsequent explosion seemed to go higher and higher. Soon, the water fired well over a hundred feet in the air. Thousands of gallons of water poured out onto the ground, following runoff streams away from the natural wonder. The show went on for several minutes, and then slowly, the bursts lessened and finally, totally subsided. The intricate, underground plumbing system of Old Faithful began refilling itself for its next miracle in an hour or so.

William ran his fingers through his hair. "Well, I guess that answers the question as to whether that is Old Faithful or not. It's pretty much unmistakable."

The friends slowly filed back to the Timer and continued getting ready for supper. They opened several large cans of stew and poured them into the blackened pot. The pot was then hung over a crackling wood fire by the steel tripod. Even at this time of year, many nights in Yellowstone were cool, and this night was no exception. They sat in a circle with their feet stretched out toward the fire and their hands thrust deep into the pockets of fleece jackets.

"Don't get your boots too close to the fire. Bob melted his soles like that one night," said William as the others laughed.

"Right, I did. And William set a pair of socks on fire one night, which was much funnier." This set off another round of laughter.

"My feet were very cold," responded William with a laugh. "It really only charred the bottom of the socks a little."

The stew soon bubbled. William took a long wooden spoon and ladled some into each bowl. It was very hot, and everyone except

Bob let theirs cool a little before beginning to eat. It was flavorful and hearty but met mixed reviews. They had been eating canned and freeze-dried food for several days now. It had gotten a little monotonous.

"I'm ready for something fresh. I'm going to catch us some fish in the morning for breakfast. I have abused my taste buds enough for a while by eating canned meals," Bob stated emphatically.

"Me too. I'll go with you," agreed Paul.

"Guys, tell you what, you catch them, I'll clean and cook them," added William. "Also, be sure to take your bear spray with you. We haven't seen any bears, but you can bet they're around here somewhere."

They sat around the fire until there were only glowing embers. Ellie put out the fire by pouring some water from one of their collapsible water buckets. They all climbed the ladder and crept into their sleeping bags. They now slept in their socks as the nylon lining of the sleeping bags was cold when they first crawled in.

The next morning, Bob was as usual awake at first light. After lying in bed a few minutes, he decided to get up and get a fire going. He quietly climbed the ladder in his stocking feet, emerging from the hatch onto the top deck. He was greeted by a sight that almost made him fall back down the ladder. Leaning down, he stuck his head in the hatch and called a warning to the others.

"Wake up, everyone. We've got visitors."

They greeted this with groans and yawns, and someone threw a boot at Bob's legs. Obviously, they preferred sleep over a dubious wake-up call.

"Why the wake-up call?" asked William sleepily.

"Come up and see," Bob said quietly as he raised his head out of the hatch.

Bob turned and quickly counted twelve Indian braves patiently sitting in a semicircle on their horses, watching the Timer. Now, they watched him as well. Several spoke, and others pointed excitedly at Bob.

The crew came scrambling up the ladder, and now both groups stared at each other in silence and awe. That was…until Spear appeared.

Spear climbed through the hatch, and a big smile broke out on his face. He peered into the faces of the newcomers, one by one. He then appeared to be calling them by name, and they smiled and called back to him. Spear climbed down from the Timer and, with a slight limp, walked over to the mounted warriors.

It was obvious they knew one another and were glad to see each other. The horses pranced around as the Indians began to speak so rapidly even Ellie could not keep up with them. She had tried to translate for the others but quickly lost track of the conversation.

Spear turned to the Timer and waved his hand in a motion that told the others to climb down and join them. He spoke briefly to Ellie and then pivoted back to the newcomers. This was greeted by nodding of the heads, but no more words were spoken. The braves climbed down from their horses and hobbled them with short lengths of grass rope. They had several spare ponies, and these were also hobbled. Then they filed past Spear and sat down around the fire ring. The horses immediately walked away and began to graze on tufts of dried grass.

Ellie enlightened the others as they climbed down the ladder from the Timer. "Spear says they are from his tribe and are his friends."

"I sure hope they're friendly," said Bob, and he eyed the bows, arrows, and spears.

Spear stacked some of the dried wood they collected the previous night. He then broke off some of the small branches and formed them into the now-familiar tepee shape. Taking out his pocketknife, he flipped the blade open with his thumbnail to murmuring from the braves. Spear ran the knife edge down the wood, producing long, slender shavings, which he then placed in the middle of the tepee. Here is where the magic began. He reached into his pocket and produced the red plastic Bic lighter.

His old friends gasped in amazement when he spun the lighter's sparking wheel and the flame appeared. He dropped to both knees and leaned over the fire ring and the wooden tepee. Reaching down, he touched the flame to the shavings, and they immediately flared up. The fire quickly spread to the smaller pieces of wood and on to the larger pieces added on top. He soon had a roaring fire going. Spear flicked the flame of the lighter on and off to the wonderment of the other members of his tribe. The braves now looked at him almost in reverence.

Ellie, unnoticed, had reentered the Timer during the excitement. She climbed down the ladder with a container from their meager kitchen supplies and some packages of Kool-Aid. She dumped the Kool-Aid into the clear plastic container, added several scoops of precious sugar, and finally added water they had taken from a spring the night before and screwed on the top. Upon vigorous shaking, the Kool-Aid turned the water a bright red, and Ellie informed them it was her favorite, cherry. She leaned close to Spear and said a few words. He walked over and talked briefly with his now dismounted friends.

Spear took the container of Kool-Aid and drank a swallow. He then spoke softly to one of his tribesmen and indicated they do the same. A handsome, brave, taller than the rest took the container, had a swallow, and broke into a big smile. He then passed it to the man standing beside him, who took a drink then passed it along to the others. By the time, it had made it through all twelve, the container was almost empty and each had a smile on his face.

Ellie reached out and took back the container. She put some fresh water into it, swished it around, and poured it out. Now everyone watched her intently. She reached into her coverall pocket, took out another packet of Kool-Aid, and showed it to her enraptured audience. She poured this packet into the container, added sugar and water, and it magically turned green! There was excited whispering among the Indians, and several even softly clapped their hands. She could tell Spear's friends thought this magic, and strong magic indeed. She reached into the container, stirred the contents with an index finger, and handed it to Spear.

Before taking a sip, Spear did a funny thing. Looking around at his circle of friends, he stuck out his tongue. It was a bright crimson!

His friends, both new and old, reacted the same way. Their eyes widened, and they had a hearty laugh.

Spear now took his obligatory sip and started the lime Kool-Aid around his circle of friends. A few minutes later, the lime-flavored Kool-Aid was also gone. Now all the drinkers were sticking out their tongues, and they all laughed until tears ran down their cheeks. Ellie had to hold her side; she was laughing so hard.

"This is like *Dances with Wolves* with a twist." William was able to choke out through his laughing.

Ellie retrieved another package she had kept in a paper bag, walking to each man, and passing out sugar cookies. She took the last one for herself and stuck her tongue to it. The guests followed suit, and even bigger smiles broke out as they sampled the sweet treats. It was amusing how different their eating methods were. Several ate their cookies in tiny nibbles, and others popped entire cookies in their mouths all at once. It seemed each method enjoyed the cookies immensely. Several even saved one of their cookies by placing them in the small deerskin pouches they carried.

Spear pointed to each of his new friends in turn and, with accompanying words, said their name. It soon became evident; the warriors were very impressed with the food, the Timer, and Bob.

Several walked over to the Timer, running their hands down its side. One rapped it with his knuckles. Another was bold enough to climb the ladder and look at the top deck. When he climbed down, all the others filed up the ladder to look.

Then there was Bob. They walked over to him and gazed in amazement. It was obvious to the crew that the newcomers had never seen anyone his size. One prodded his chest with an index finger. Another reached up and squeezed his bicep. Bob, being the ham he was, drew his right arm parallel to the ground and tightened his bicep into a huge sphere of muscle. There were low, indistinct sounds of appreciation. Bob, very pleased with himself, dropped his arm back to his side. To complete the show, Bob turned to one of the larger braves and beckoned him to come closer. This he did, with obvious trepidation. Bob reached out to his assistant and placed his hands on each arm just below the shoulder. With arms held straight, he lifted the warrior off the ground and held him in midair. This resulted not in low, indistinct sounds of appreciation but in whoops and yells. With a triumphant smile, Bob gently placed him back on the ground. The brave stared at Bob so hard it seemed his eyes would pop out. He turned to his companions, laughed, and gave a little hop in the air.

"Wow, show's over!" said William. "Let's fix breakfast for everyone. We can see if they like the rest of our food."

"Or rather what's left of our food," Bob softly intoned, but William knew Bob had a generous heart and was glad to share.

William, Paul, and Ellie started preparing oatmeal, heavily flavoring it with cinnamon, dried fruit, and sugar. Bob and Spear added wood to the fire, and soon the oatmeal bubbled. Splendid odors filled the air, and more than a few mouths watered in anticipation.

Bob returned from the Timer with the eight cups he had been able to find. After conferring with Spear, Ellie said the braves would not mind sharing.

Ellie and Paul filled each cup to the brim and passed them out. Ellie held a cup and blew on, hoping this indicated it might be hot. Hot did not seem to matter. The men dipped their fingers into the cups and transferred the hot mixture to their mouths. Each smiled, and several spoke to Spear in a rapid cadence.

Spear turned to the cooks. "They like it much. We don't have much what you call sweet here. They like much."

The "sweet" came out as "swat," but all knew what it meant. The meal had proved to be a hit.

CHAPTER 23

LOSING A FRIEND

WHILE THE OATMEAL was being consumed, Ellie and Paul were huddled by the fire preparing one last course. "William, Bob, let's take their cups and clean them. I have one more item on the menu," Ellie ordered as she went back into the Timer and their dwindling supply of food.

After the cups were cleaned and wiped dry, Ellie came out with hot chocolate. After mixing and heating the ingredients, she motioned for them to come closer. As they gathered around, Paul filled each cup with the steaming, creamy liquid. The cups were passed around, and the hot, almost bittersweet drink produced more smiles and more compliments for the cook.

As their new friends were finishing off the hot chocolate, the cooks, prompted by Bob, fixed some more oatmeal for the original crew. They all gathered around the fire to have their breakfast. William and Paul tossed more kindling on the fire as the mornings continued to be cool. While they were enjoying their meals, Spear had moved apart with his tribesmen and appeared to be engaged in a deep discussion with them.

Spear talked for an hour with his old friends. He occasionally turned and updated his new friends on what was being said. In some of the conversation, he turned to Ellie first to translate. She would talk with Spear and then repeat in English to the others what he had said.

Finally, they appeared to have finished their discussion. After conferring with Ellie, and with a long, sad face, Spear turned to the crew. "They travel back to our home." After a long pause, "Expect me to go with them."

The crew stared with shocked, stunned faces at Spear. They had not considered this possibility. In a short period of time, they had come to consider Spear a part of their company and even more importantly a friend. This revelation hurt.

Ellie looked around at the others and then back at Spear. "I really had not thought about you leaving." Then realizing she had spoken in English, she repeated approximately the same sentiments in his language.

"Me too," chimed in Bob.

"Me three," added Paul.

Shaking his head in obvious distress, William looked Spear in the eye. "Spear, you do what you need to do, but we will really miss you. I'm sure you have friends and family that miss you, and I know that's not easy."

Turning to the others, William added, "I hope he understood some of that."

Ellie leaned in. "I bet he did. Spear's parents are both dead. He has no brothers or sisters. His parents were killed in a raid by the Blackfeet several years ago. He has friends but no family. Golly, he sounds like the rest of us."

Spear walked forward and put out his hand to each member of the crew. Ellie reached up and hugged him, saying, "I think I need to go away for a few minutes." She got to her feet, walked past the gathering and through the small grove of trees to be alone for a few minutes.

The others nodded their heads, and Spear began to gather up his few belongings. He turned to Bob and held out his hand. "This yours." In his hand was the lighter he had used to start so many fires.

With a grim smile, Bob reached out and closed Spear's hand around the lighter. "No, that's yours." Then he turned to William and Paul. "I wonder what people will think if that ever turns up in the future?" he said with a quizzical look on his face.

"I doubt very seriously it will make it intact that long," responded his brother.

Spear walked over to his Indian friends. As a group, they turned, walked to their hobbled ponies, untied them, and mounted up. In single file, the tribesmen kicked their horses into a slow trot and rode west without a backward glance. As they passed into some trees, Spear wheeled his horse around, reared him up, and waved. With that, he rode out of sight and seemingly out of their lives. He would be missed.

William kicked an unburned piece of wood into the fire with the toe of his boot. "It's hard to imagine getting that close to someone so quickly."

"Wow, it's sure hard to see him leave!" agreed Ellie as she walked up, joining the others. "I can't believe he's really gone."

"Let's hang around here today. I really don't feel like moving. We can watch Old Faithful some more," said Paul gloomily.

It was decided they would stay at Old Faithful and leave early the next morning. It would also give them time to finish some needed chores like mending and washing their clothes. Maybe it would also help each one to get over the dismal feeling left by their friend's departure.

The crew spent part of the afternoon at the Firehole River beating their clothes with the many handy rocks. They were amazed how this cleaned their clothes even without soap. The clothes were then spread out over bushes to dry. Each piece had only to be turned once and was soon dry. The clothes were then examined for rips, tears, and missing buttons. William produced a sewing kit, and soon, the necessary repairs were being made. The dried and repaired items were neatly folded and stored away in the Timer.

The crew, now reduced to four, ate a light lunch and supper. Bob again expressed his desire to catch some fresh fish for breakfast in the morning. Paul said he was tired and would sleep late and would leave the fishing to Bob. The group was quiet that night with very little conversation. The fact was they missed their friend. As the fire died down, they crawled into the sleeping bags and were soon fast asleep.

The next morning, Bob was up with the sun. Moving quietly to avoid waking the others, he gathered up his fly rod and a handful of flies and headed for the river. It was a cool morning, and with the rising sun glittering off the iron-colored river, it seemed a perfect morning for fishing. Others had different plans.

The fish weren't biting. He had moved and had changed flies several times but to no avail. As he was thinking what he needed to do to change his luck, he heard some rocks shift behind him. He quickly reached for his bear spray when a voice stopped him.

"Leave it alone!"

Bob slowly turned, and there stood his huge adversary from the other timer with an evil sneer on his face. He was taking no chances with Bob this time. He was holding a shiny, black handgun which was aimed at the center of Bob's chest.

"I have been looking forward to this for a long time. I have finally caught up with you."

Bob looked over his shoulder, back toward the Timer and his friends. If only there was some way to warn them.

"Your friends may see us, but that's no problem for me. I have you, and you are not getting away this time. Also, this is a big, open area. We can easily run them down with our faster ship."

Glancing one more time back at the Timer, Bob could see activity, but it was too far away to tell what was going on. Then he saw the Timer lift and slowly start north. Did they not realize he wasn't aboard? Couldn't they see what was happening? Well, he would at least see if he could keep this guy occupied for a few minutes. Maybe if he could stall this guy, they would have a better chance at escape.

"You better be careful. We might just run you down or maybe just run over you."

"Even now, you still have the big mouth. I think I will shoot you in the leg before we start back. I want to take no chance on losing you."

"I'm too big to carry. How are you going to get me back if you shoot me?"

"I won't shoot you too badly, just enough to slow you down. Do not worry. I will make you walk back no matter what." This he stated with an evil implication that left no doubt he would do exactly what he said. He would make Bob walk to the enemy timer no matter what it took.

He then smiled his sinister and cruel smile and slowly lowered the gun toward Bob's legs. Bob visibly tensed, but he refused to beg or show fear. As he watched, the right index finger tightened and slowly began to squeeze the trigger.

Suddenly, there was a whizzing sound in the air, and an arrow appeared in the fiend's right leg just above the knee. The giant screamed, dropped his gun, and fell to his knees. He clutched his leg with both hands, obviously giving no further thought to Bob.

Bob immediately spun and bounded away in the direction he last saw the Timer headed. Several shots whistled over his head as he ran. Looking back, he was not surprised to see the wounded villain sitting on the ground, firing at him. Just then, the other timer emerged from the trees and started after him. It was only a little over two hundred yards away, and he knew there was no chance he could outdistance them. It would be sure to catch him before he could reach his friends. Still, he was going to give it a try. He did wonder about the arrow, but now was no time to stop and thank someone.

As he ran, he heard pounding hooves, which seemed to be getting closer. Bob stole a quick glance, and there was Spear flying toward him on a large brown-and-white dappled pony. As Spear reached him, he reined in the horse with his left hand and reached down with his right to Bob. They grabbed each other's wrist, and Bob vaulted onto the horse behind Spear. The horse gave a tremble, reared, and sped away in a hard run with Bob's arms wrapped tightly around Spear's waist. As Spear and Bob watched, their Timer emerged from a grove of trees and took a course that would intersect with them. Maybe there was a chance, if only a slim chance, they could make their escape after all.

Their horse stumbled slightly but kept going. He was doing his best, but he was carrying more weight than he could manage. His labored breathing testified to this fact. Spear leaned forward on his neck and with hands and voice urged on his mount.

Spear turned his head slightly toward Bob. "He can run like the wind, but we are too much for him." Bob knew he meant too much weight. He decided if it appeared they would be caught, he would jump off and let Spear get away.

As if their friends on the Timer realized their dilemma, their angle toward them increased. They closed the distance rapidly, but so did their pursuers. They heard the whine of bullets flying past them, but thankfully, neither man nor horse had been struck.

When the Timer was within fifty yards, Bob straightened up and waved his arm for them to move away in the same direction they were riding. Paul immediately caught the intent of the message, slowed, and then bore away on the same course as Spear and Bob. This was away from the enemy timer and down toward the fast-approaching Firehole River. They knew that whatever happened, it had to occur before the river, which would stop them in their tracks. There was no way the horse could carry a double load through the water and up the opposite bank.

With a few more jumps of their powerful steed, Spear and Bob pulled even with the Timer. Spear pointed to the ladder and looked back at Bob. Bob leaned over and grasped the ladder in his right hand and swung off the horse. Bob's legs crashed into the side of the Timer, but he was able to hold on. Swinging his feet to one of the lower rungs, he quickly pulled himself up the ladder. Spear's horse almost went to his knees with the shift of weight but was then able to regain his stride. He gathered himself and, with the reduced weight, quickly caught up with the Timer. As he pulled even with the ladder, Spear leaped off the horse's back onto the ladder, like a circus rider. At the same time, he pulled the bridle out of the horse's mouth and off his head. The horse slowed and began to veer off to the left. Spear scampered up the ladder and darted toward the hatch as bullets rang off the Timer's sides. As he moved past William, he saw Bob in a heap on the upper deck.

"Okay?" he said in a strained voice as he looked on in concern.

Opening his eyes and looking up, Bob smiled. "I'm okay, just winded a little bit. I don't want to do that again anytime soon."

With that, and over Bob's objections, William made him and Spear climb through the hatch and down inside the Timer.

Up top, William and Paul had their hands full trying to drive, strategize, and, at the same time, stay low because of the bullets. As all this excitement was going on, they were also trying to figure out a route that might give them the best chance of escape. The other timer was only one hundred and fifty yards behind them and continued gaining at a frightening rate.

"Head for the river, Paul. It's our best bet to keep moving. We don't have time to find our way through trees. We just can't afford to pause or stop. They would be on us in a few seconds."

Paul nodded and drove the Timer through an opening in the trees and out over the Firehole River. He headed north toward Lower and Midway Geyser Basins.

William pointed down the river. "There is Grand Prismatic Spring."

Paul looked ahead to see billows of steam rising several hundred yards ahead and to the left of the riverbank. As they watched, the wind blew the steam out over the river, obscuring its surface.

"William, we don't need a tour guide. We've got to find a way out of this mess," Paul said urgently.

"I know, I know," answered William. He thought the scene looked strange without the bridge crossing over the Firehole River at Grand Prismatic.

They saw steam continuing to rise above Grand Prismatic and some other geothermal features to the left of the river. Then as William looked on, several other strange things caught his eye. A huge puff of steam suddenly appeared, and he thought he saw the ground shaking. Was he seeing things?

"Paul, steer us up the bank and toward the large plume of steam. I have an idea. I'm unsure what to do with it yet, but at least it's something. I guess a bad plan is better than no plan at all."

William looked over his shoulder and saw that the other timer had stopped firing at them. It was now less than a hundred yards behind. "They think they've got us and don't have to shoot. Their faster timer will just ride us into the ground. I bet that's it."

"I think they've got us too," Paul said with a note of resignation in his voice.

As the Timer topped the bank through the steam, Paul and William could see water splashing in the yawning maw of a great opening in the ground.

"Paul, drive straight toward that water!"

Paul looked at William with uncertainty but dutifully aimed the Timer at the heavy concentration of steam and water.

William leaned closer. "That's Excelsior Geyser, and it might save our necks. We just need a little luck on our side."

As Paul drove the Timer toward Excelsior Geyser, the splashing increased in volume, and the steam rose higher and higher. The other timer had closed to within seventy-five yards, and some of its crew was standing on the conning tower. There was a huge figure shaking a fist and shouting what seemed to be threats or curses.

William leaned down to the hatch and asked for rain jackets, which were handed up through the hatch and quickly donned by him and Paul. "Paul, put up your hood and tighten it down. I'll drive while you do it."

They quickly changed places, and Paul pulled the hood over his head and tied the strings that dangled on each side of his chin, taking only took a few seconds. Switching places, William then fastened his hood. They had barely regained their places when a wide jet of water rocketed from the gaping mouth of Excelsior. They were at the edge of the geyser, and the acidic water rained down on them in a light mist. It was hot but not unbearable.

"Paul, we're between bursts. Go another fifty yards straight ahead and then make a hard turn to the left. After that, get us out of here as fast as you can."

"Wow!" Paul said with trepidation as he looked down into the boiling cauldron of water and steam. It appeared to be pulsating with a life of its own as it seemed to crash in on itself from every angle. In a matter of seconds, they passed into the steam and lost sight of the other timer.

Paul drove the prescribed distance and made an abrupt turn to the left. The Timer's tilt caught William by surprise so that he fell from his crouching position and slid across the wet deck. He had turned over on his back with his legs in the air, and when he hit the railing, his legs and hips vaulted over the top.

"William!" screamed Paul in alarm.

As William started falling, he threw out his right arm and felt his hand hit then close on the slippery top railing. Looking down, he saw it was fifty feet to the lip of Excelsior and safety. He swung perilously above the splashing, churning waters and felt his hand slowly but surely begin to slip. He knew with certainty he would have no chance to get a second hold. The railing slid through his fingers, and he began to fall.

Suddenly, at that instant, he felt something grab the back of his jacket. He was now swinging back and forth about the maelstrom, but he was attached to Paul's muscular right arm.

"Don't worry, William. I've got you."

William felt himself slowly being lifted as his jacket pulled tight under his arms. Finally, he was able to turn his body enough to grasp the railing with both of his hands. With Paul's help, he pulled himself over the railing and landed wet and shaking on the Timer's deck. Though pale and unsteady, he heaved a great sigh of relief and stood up slowly. He threw an arm around Paul's neck and said, "Paul, you just saved me from a mighty bad way to go. I won't ever forget it."

As they cleared the edge of Excelsior with Paul back in the pilot's seat, they moved out of the steam and turned to look for their pursuer. As they watched, they both jerked back as a gigantic roar erupted from Excelsior. A blast of superheated water, hundreds of feet wide, exploded into the sky.

"William, look at that! I had no idea geysers got that big!"

"Paul, the only people living in our time that have seen a geyser that big are on these two ships. Excelsior was the biggest geyser in the world and blew itself out from this type of eruption over a hundred years ago. It was huge. I think there was once a geyser in New Zealand higher, but Excelsior was just massive."

William strained to see through the steam and water and said, "I wonder what's happening to the other timer."

Heads popped up from below. The others wanted to see the source of the mighty sound. They climbed out and joyfully joined William and Paul on the wet deck.

"There!" shouted Ellie, and she pointed through a break in the surging water and steam.

The other timer was at least fifty feet high and spinning along its axis. As they watched, it broke out of the steam and water and slowly spun to earth. It hit on its conning tower and settled on its side. Luckily for those inside, it fell outside the rim of the geyser. The friends broke into a cheer. They were saved, and again, it was Mother Nature to the rescue.

William turned to the others. "Excelsior Geyser is in its glory days. It's the biggest geyser in recorded history, and it saved us this time. I do hope the people in that timer are okay as strange as that sounds."

"I hope so as well, and I don't believe we'll be seeing them anymore," said Bob with enthusiasm.

"I don't know about that. When I was trying to get to William, I think I saw their top hatch being closed from the inside and nobody up top. They may be banged around a bit, but I think their ship is probably still operational."

As they watched, an escape hatch opened in the side of the conning tower of the other timer. Several figures tumbled out, including a tall, angry, shouting man limping around on a heavily bandaged leg.

"There's my buddy, I guess he is okay," said Bob as he got to his feet and waved. He smiled and gave a hearty laugh as the other man returned to fist waving, threat shouting an insults. "Look at that, he will never learn." Cupping his hands, Bob yelled back, "I hope you guys had fun. It sure was fun watching."

"Wait, wait pictures!" Ellie scrambled below and returned with two cameras. Handing one camera to Bob, she began filming the Excelsior's eruption with the other. Bob raised the still camera and madly snapped photos. This would be some unique documentation. They wondered how many people would ever see the pictures. Probably not too many was the consensus.

William clapped Paul on his broad back. "Get us out of here. Steer straight down the Firehole. I think I know the best way out of here."

CHAPTER 24

A CLOSE CALL

PAUL DROVE THE Timer over the edge of the spectacularly colored Grand Prismatic Spring and out over the Firehole River. Midstream, the craft turned and headed north, exiting Midway Geyser Basin.

As Paul drove them down the river, William pondered how their luck could be so bad that they continued to run into the other timer. There was no probable way this could happen so often in this huge country. "We've got to figure out how they keep finding us. It's too much of a coincidence that they keep turning up where we are. It just doesn't add up."

"They would need something like a homing device on our Timer. As far as I know, they haven't gotten near it," replied an equally puzzled Bob.

Ellie put her chin in the palm of her left hand and then snapped her fingers. "Spear, pull up your pants legs."

With a perplexed look on his face, Spear leaned forward and pulled up both pants legs. There on his left ankle was a metal ring about a quarter of an inch thick. Attached to the ring was a small square of the same grayish metal dangling from it. Spear reached down and in haltering English said, "They put on leg, captured." He then flicked the metal square with an index finger, causing it to make a tinkling sound.

Ellie reached over and grasped the square. "There is your homing device, I would bet anything. I remember seeing it when I treated

Spear's leg. I thought it was something of his, and things were happening pretty fast about that time."

"Do you think they did this to track us?" asked Paul.

"No way. They did it to catch Spear if he tried to escape," said Bob as he reached and gave the ring a tug, lifting Spear's left foot off the deck.

"Okay, how do we get it off?" asked William, annoyed.

Bob reached down and took Spear's arm. "Come on, I think I've got some bolt cutters below that can handle this job."

"I think you better do that below. I hear a waterfall, rapids, or something ahead," offered Paul.

"Good idea. That's probably Firehole Falls or the rapids," replied William.

Ellie and Bob took Spear below as the Timer passed over a long stretch of white water and rapids. Here the river narrowed, and the sides seem to slide in toward them. Suddenly, they were at the edge of a drop where the water poured over the lip and fell sixty feet in a great torrent to the river below. Without hesitation, Paul expertly flew over the edge and dropped the Timer down to fifteen feet above the river. This had become known as its traveling height. The immediate sensation had been one of falling. This changed, as they fell, to the feeling of landing on a cushion of air.

William sat against the railing, quiet for several minutes. Suddenly, he snapped his fingers. "I've got an idea, Paul!"

He then leaned down to the hatch. "Hurry, Bob, get that homing thing off Spear."

"It's really tough metal, but I can cut it off. No, not your foot, Spear." Shortly, Bob reached up from below and handed William the severed ring. It had been sawed through, leaving a narrow opening. Bob used his considerable strength to stretch it enough to slip it over the Spear's ankle off his foot.

Taking the ring, William stood up and pointed downriver. "Those cliffs ahead look familiar. We should be getting to the Madison River in a few minutes. Paul, when we get there, put us down on one of the banks near some driftwood."

"Will do."

Two minutes later, they saw the Madison River through the trees. Paul drove the Timer to the far bank and set it down near a large pile of twisted, gnarled driftwood.

William hurried below and returned with a short piece of rope and the homing device. He climbed down the exterior ladder and sorted through the wood that had been deposited by spring floods. Presently, he selected a thick piece about two feet long. He carefully looped the rope through the ring and tied it securely to the wood.

"That is one good idea!" said his smiling brother.

William heaved the piece of wood, offending ring attached, out into midstream. The current caught the wood and swirled it merrily on its way to the west.

At William's instructions, the Timer started its way east to the crew's cheers and laughter. They generally agreed how much they wished they could see the face of Bob's "friend" when he discovered their trick.

William told the others to gather around so he could tell them his plan. "That little diversion will buy us some time, but let's not take any unnecessary chances. We will cut no more trees unless necessary. We don't want to leave a trail of any kind. We'll hide any fires we build and make sure we break up any fire rings and scatter the ashes. Let's cover as much distance as possible today before we stop for the night. Paul is going to follow the Gibbon River, which will lead us north away from this area and our friends on the other timer."

The others agreed and Paul said, "Aye, aye, skipper." It was the first time William's leadership was verbally recognized. It had been understood for days.

Looking at his brother, William asked, "Did you catch any fish this morning?"

"Not a one. I guess they weren't biting."

William laughed. "I forgot to tell you. Firehole Falls cuts off migrating fish. Until they started stocking, there were no fish in the Firehole above the falls."

"Well, that explains it! I knew I was too good a fisherman to not catch anything," said Bob, slapping his thigh.

It was smooth sailing for Paul until they reached Gibbon Falls. Bob said he had been worried about how they would get over it. The falls did not prove to be a problem for Paul's expert driving at all. Even though eighty feet high, the fan-shaped falls fell at a moderate slant. Through some judicious switchback driving, Paul was able to get them to the top and then on upriver.

They turned east at what Bob and William hoped was the future site of Norris Junction. William told Paul to go east and stop at the first lake they came to. He said this should be Wolf Lake and intended for them to spend the night there.

"William, what if we don't come to a lake?" asked Paul.

"Then I guess Bob told you to turn at the wrong place."

This elicited a grin from Bob, who gave his brother a light punch to the shoulder.

"Well," said William, "we'll stop somewhere for the night. Tomorrow, we'll sort out the next landmark for us to shoot for and plan our next moves." With that, he lay back and covered his eyes with the brim of his cap.

Bob and William's reckoning had proved to be good. Just after dark, Paul drove the Timer out over a body of water, which Bob confirmed to be Wolf Lake as he shook his brother awake.

They decided they would have a cold camp at least for that night. They ate a hastily prepared meal then went below and settled into their sleeping bags to talk.

William leaned back against the bulkhead, reached over, and tugged at Spear's fleece jacket. "Spear, I have to ask, why did you come back? We are all so glad."

Spear looked down before answering, "William, no family with my tribe, all gone. All you now Spear's family, that's why."

Ellie slid over to Spear and gave him a hug, which drew an embarrassed smile.

"This was one exciting day," said Bob emphatically. "I don't know what would have happened if Spear hadn't come along and picked me up on his horse."

"Gee, think about what the horse felt like when you hopped aboard." Chuckled his brother.

Then from above, Ellie said, "Hey guys, get up here." Ellie had leaned down into the hatch.

The rest of the crew quickly unzipped their sleeping bags and, expecting trouble, fairly flew up the ladder. When they reached the deck, they saw large, fluffy snowflakes silently dropping on the Timer. Slowly, it was turning it white. The metallic surface was giving way to a soft, white layer coating the craft's upper deck.

"Yellowstone is a really different kind of place," observed Paul. "You hear it can snow here every month of the year, but you don't believe it until you see it."

They handed up warm jackets and sat for an hour, watching the snowflakes gently paint their ship. Bob had given Spear one of his jackets, and it created a comical sight. It extended well down his legs, and his hands would not reach the end of the sleeves, but it did keep him warm. Finally, they blew on their hands and shook the snow off their shoulders and pants and dropped down the hatch and went to sleep.

The next morning, they ate and then watched William as he brought out a map. He was drawing lines to the east and southeast using a pencil and ruler.

"I really wanted to see the hot springs at Mammoth, but I guess we better save that for another trip. I think it's just too much of a risk of running into our friends on the other timer," William said, sadly shaking of his head.

"We've got to quit referring to those on the other timer as 'our friends.' It has poor Spear badly confused," Ellie said as she patted Spear's arm.

"Sorry, I agree," said William as he spun the map around so that everyone could see it. "We're going to hit the Yellowstone River and follow it as far as we can. We may have to improvise as we go, but that's how I think we need to start out. It'll give us a track to follow so we don't get lost."

William pulled out his compass and pointed out a course away from Wolf Lake. This route led through an area of large, old-growth trees with plenty of room between them and very little underbrush. Paul slid into the driver's seat and started off on that path. Initially, they had to ease between a few of the trees, but as they drifted away from the lake's edge, the trees thinned, and the going became easier.

William looked at the others gathered around him. "I'm going to try to find the Yellowstone at the Grand Canyon. Since we're this close, I think we should check it out. It will be interesting to see if it's changed much if any over the years."

The Timer cruised along, following William's compass heading through a forested area of lodgepole pines. When they came to some areas that had been burned, they stayed over open meadows left by the fires These meadows were carpeted with flowers in colors of blue, white, and red.

The open areas allowed Paul to better see where he was going. He followed the contours of ridges and ravines as they continued in the general direction William wanted to go. After several hours of this leisure flying, the Timer topped a ridge. Ahead, in the distance, they saw a long line of rising mist.

Shielding his eyes from the morning sun, Bob said, "That's got to be the Yellowstone."

William pointed slightly to the southeast. "Paul, head where the mist ends. I think that might be just beyond the Lower Falls."

CHAPTER 25

GRAND CANYON OF THE YELLOWSTONE

PAUL FOLLOWED THE ridge as it led down toward the mist, the anticipation increasing by the minute. The ridge had been burned over, and traveling along its spine was quite easy. As the ridge petered out, they entered a mountain meadow followed by a grove of trees. Fortunately, the fire had left several paths through the forest, and they had no problem making progress. The mist drew ever closer, and now a sound like thunder came to their ears. Paul drove the Timer toward the sound, using it as a guiding point. In a few minutes, through an opening in the trees, they glimpsed the Grand Canyon of the Yellowstone. Its grandeur never failed to inspire those seeing it for the first time.

As they moved closer, William said almost in a whisper, "And that is where Yellowstone gets its name."

They looked on at the steep sides of a huge canyon streaked with yellow. There was a drop of hundreds of feet to the Yellowstone River which ran like a silver thread at the bottom of the chasm.

"These canyon walls have a lot of iron in them. Also, some of the colors are caused by oxidation. It's quite a sight. Paul, don't get too close to the edge. It's a long way to the bottom. If we went over, we probably wouldn't hit, but it would be a jarring stop from such a big drop," William said with more than a hint of warning in his voice.

As they drove along the north rim, Bob pointed out Artist Point on the opposite side of the canyon. Paul was able to afford them a great view of the entire south side. Even though they looked, their side was too steep to find the path that led to the lip of the Lower Falls.

Looking down the awful drop, Bob said, "Can you imagine what it took to build a path down that wall?"

"I don't even want to think about it. Completed, it hangs over the canyon with a guardrail, the only thing between you and a sheer drop," William said with a grimace.

"Did people really crawl out on Artist Point and paint with those awful drops on each side?"

William laughed. "They sure did. They carried all their gear out there, set up, and happily painted away. Pretty amazing they were able to do that. I think I would get dizzy just looking over the edge."

"William, how did it get its name?" asked Ellie.

"The story I have heard is that the park's most famous photographer, F. Jay Haynes, named it. He thought Thomas Moran had painted the Lower Falls from that point. Actually, he painted it from this side."

"Let's get going, Paul, our professor can keep us here all day with stories about the park. William, tell them later about the hotel that used to be at the canyon, it's kind of interesting," Bob said with a look of sincere admiration for his brother.

As they moved upriver, the group turned to the beautiful Lower Falls of the Yellowstone. The river roared over the lip and crashed three hundred feet later into a frothing, splashing exuberance of white water.

"The Lower Falls is higher than the Upper Falls. That's another quirky thing with names in Yellowstone. It's a little over fifty feet higher than Union Falls in Cascade Corner. Someday, I would really like to show you Union Falls. You would quickly understand where it got its name," said William. "You know, there is something different about the Lower Falls. I can't figure out what it is."

"I know what it is," responded his brother.

"What?"

"The green stripe is gone."

"You're right. That is exactly what it is!"

"A green stripe?" asked a perplexed Paul.

"Yes, a green stripe." Laughed William. "In the future, the Lower Falls has a bright green stripe in the water as it falls over the edge. It starts at the lip and falls a quarter of the way to the bottom."

"Why is there a bright green stripe, Professor William?" asked a curious Ellie.

"Since you asked nicely, I'll tell you. There is a notch in the lip that lets deeper water flow over the edge at that point. Because that water is deeper, it has a darker green color. And that is your answer, Miss Heath."

Paul flew the Timer along the edge of the canyon, and they soon put the Lower Falls behind them. Directly ahead, they saw the Upper Falls.

After studying the situation for a minute, William turned to their pilot. "Paul, stay on the edge as much as possible. No need to go out on the river with the hundred-foot Upper Falls right in front of us. If we can't follow the bank, we'll either have to backtrack or find a way through these woods."

"Let's try going ahead, William. I think I can ease us along the edge," replied Paul warily.

Paul carefully followed the canyon's edge, at times too close for comfort, but he eventually made it past the Upper Falls. He then eased the Timer down a low bank and out over the center of Yellowstone River.

As Paul drove to midstream, Bob remarked on the Upper Falls. "You know, in lots of places, the Upper Falls would be a real tourist attraction. In Yellowstone, the visual competition is just too great. There are so many things to see, including other falls. It kind of gets lost in the shuffle."

CHAPTER 26

HAYDEN VALLEY: THE EDEN OF THE AMERICAN WEST

AFTER PASSING THE Upper Falls, Paul had no obstacles from that point to Yellowstone Lake. He settled the Timer midstream, and away they went. This stretch would prove to be a wonderful part of their journey. The Yellowstone was sun-dappled and crowded with birds. There were ducks, Canadian geese, beautiful trumpeter swans, and, in the shallows, great blue herons. Manning sentinel in the trees were osprey and bald eagles. The birds on the river were noisy and fled out of the way of the Timer but seldom took flight. It was almost as if they recognized a kindred spirit. The crew lined the railing, spellbound by the numbers and variety of the many birds. There was lots of filming and picture taking being done. This new commitment to the cameras was paying dividends.

Twice they saw huge moose standing belly deep in the water, eating. They had green vegetation hanging from their mouths, unperturbed by human presence. On neither occasion did they bolt for safety. Their whiskered heads turned and followed the Timer on its flight up the river. They seemed more interested in filling their stomachs than fleeing from the intruders.

They also saw dozens of elk in clearings along the river. Their coats were sleek and shiny as they put on weight to prepare for the harsh Yellowstone winter looming only a few months ahead.

183

Deer were everywhere, and Bob marveled at the size of the antlers on some of the bucks. "For bucks to get antlers that size, they have to live a long time. This is what you get when you don't have hunters carrying rifles with scopes."

"Look over there!" exclaimed Ellie excitedly. On the right bank were two cubs that looked like teddy bears. They stood on their hind legs, their little, round ears perking up as they regarded the Timer. "Stop, Paul, and let me take some pictures."

As Ellie scrambled for her camera, an enormous mother grizzly came out from behind a downed tree. She stood up, roared at the Timer, and then chased her young back through the trees. All the while Ellie was madly filming away, getting footage of the action.

"Think I got some good shots," she said. "I should have been filming all along. I guess I got a little overwhelmed with all we were seeing."

Soon, they left the wooded region behind and passed into the more open range of Hayden Valley. Thousands of bison were scattered across the wide plains. They were on the sides of rolling hills, in the center marshy area, and in the water. As the friends watched, a herd of several hundred walked into the river and began swimming for the opposite bank. Paul stopped the Timer, and they watched in fascination. Even calves seemed to have no problem making the swim.

As they sat watching, each of them heard crashing noises. Looking in the direction of the sound, they could see dust rising from a flat area several hundred yard up the river. Paul drove the Timer in that direction and stopped again so they could watch. Two giant bulls were pawing the ground with their huge heads lowered. As if by some unheard signal, they rushed forward and crashed into one another. They swirled around in what seemed almost a dance. Each stood at least six and a half feet tall at the shoulder, and neither showed signs of backing down. They continued ramming their heads against each other until one was finally forced to his knees. The other bull immediately gored him and rolled him over. The vanquished bull struggled to his feet and limped away in defeat. The winner made a short run at him, turned, and majestically ambled back to the herd.

"Wow, what was that all about? It was like they were trying to kill each other," Paul said with awe in his voice.

"Mating season," answered Bob.

"Boys!" Ellie chimed in.

"There!" said William as the others turned to look at what he was pointing at.

A pack of eight wolves came loping over a rise. They varied in color from dark tan to black and were moving fast. They headed for a small herd of about fifty bulls, cows, and calves. The bison, alerted to their presence, started galloping along the river. The cows and calves were in the front, the bulls keeping station at the rear. The wolves quickly split into two groups on each side of the running bison. They drove two wedges into the running bison, and the pack began to isolate eight to ten cows and calves and maneuver them away from the main herd. Next, they chased this small group away to the right. They disappeared over a hill and down into the valley beyond.

William shook his head. "Those are real hunters. Did you see the size of the two black ones in the lead?"

The others nodded their heads in agreement. Spear looked at Ellie and said several words the others did not understand. While doing this, he also made several hand signs.

"He said the wolves will eat well tonight," reported Ellie, with an arching of her eyebrows.

The group continued their cruise up the Yellowstone, seeing more birds and other animals than they could count. It was obvious that these creatures had little experience with people and probably even less with flying machines. There was little or no fear in their actions or attitudes.

Suddenly, Ellie put her hand to her nose. "What is that smell?" She gasped as the strong smell of rotten eggs swept over the crew.

"I think I know," said William. "I believe it's the Sulphur Caldron."

"Paul, when you see a low spot on the bank, go up it and drive us to the right. We should be able to find Sulphur Caldron with no trouble."

"I would think we could find it with our eyes closed," Ellie said as she screwed up her nose.

Paul soon found a low, swampy bank and drove the Timer between two trees, up, and over the west bank. William directed him south; the sulfur odor became stronger and stronger the farther they went.

"Look over there," William said as he pointed out the Sulphur Caldron's yellow, churning waters which roiled and pitched in an oval pit as though it was alive. Paul set the Timer down above it.

"That's one of the most acidic springs in Yellowstone," William observed after they had watched it a few minutes. He then gave Paul thumbs-up, and they lifted off and started back south.

They had traveled only a short way when a roaring sound came from the direction they were flying. Paul corrected their course a little to the right and drove toward the noise.

"Something is strange about those trees ahead," Bob said, perplexed.

The others craned their necks to get a good look at where Bob pointed. As they approached, they could see the trees were covered in a blackish, gray paste. About that time, there was another roar, and a large gout of mud arched through the air and crashed down among the trees in front of them.

"Is that the Mud Volcano, William?" asked Bob.

"I think so."

Paul eased the Timer through some of the mud-coated trees. Suddenly, there in front of them was the thirty-foot-high Mud Volcano. The trees surrounding the volcano were coated with the mud it heaved out. The more recent wet mud was dark while the drier mud was numerous lighter shades. Paul stopped the Timer a safe distance away, and they watched the volcano erupt several more times, flinging mud high in the air and many feet away.

"Can you imagine what people in our time would do if they could see eruptions like these?" asked Paul.

William smiled. "They would be impressed."

"It doesn't erupt any longer, William?" asked Ellie.

"Nope, it doesn't. I told you there would be some strange sights to see in Yellowstone. Some like this one are strange to me."

Continuing southeast, they spotted Black Dragon Caldron in the distance and passed over Sizzling Basin. When they saw Elephant Back Mountain standing eight hundred feet above them, they knew they were almost at Yellowstone Lake. After a short search, Paul found the river and drove the Timer out over it. The inland trees had become too thick for easy traveling.

After a few more minutes, they emerged on beautiful Yellowstone Lake. The lovely blue of the lake and sky framed against the backdrop of the rugged Absaroka Mountains was a sight they wouldn't soon forget.

Paul leaned back in his seat and turned to William. "Wow! That looks like an ocean!"

"It's the largest freshwater lake above seven thousand feet in the US. It's a nice lake," William added appreciatively.

"Paul, look straight ahead. Do you see that island? Drive us over there. That's Stevenson Island. Bears sometimes get stuck out there by walking out on the ice and not coming back before it thaws. I think that might be a good spot to spend the night."

"William 'Mr. Answer Man,' who was Stevenson?" asked Ellie.

"He was an assistant to Ferdinand Hayden who surveyed Yellowstone in 1871. He got an island and a mountain named after him."

"Now, I think I would like an island or mountain named after me," Paul stated in a semiserious voice.

Pointing to a spit of land sticking out in the lake, Bob asked William, "Is that where Lake Hotel is going to be?"

"I think so. I believe in less than a hundred years, it will be on that bulge into the lake."

"Which way do we go, William?" asked Paul.

"I wish we had time to explore West Thumb Geyser Basin, but I think it might be a good idea to get settled in and out of sight for the night. Head due south, Paul. We'll spend the night on Frank Island."

CHAPTER 27

SOUTH AND OUT
OF THE PARK

As William suggested, Paul drove the Timer out over the lake and due south. A breeze had sprung up, and there were small whitecaps on the huge body of water. Bob said that the lake was so clean you could safely drink out of it.

As they sailed south, Bob looked down at the long, narrow shape of Stevenson Island and said, "Next stop, Frank Island and supper. It's probably only six to eight miles."

Soon, another larger island loomed dead ahead. Paul directed the Timer toward it, circled it, and spotted a small clearing just back from the rocky shore. He nestled their craft in among some small trees and set it on the ground. The crew immediately climbed out and cut some limbs from the nearby trees, careful not to damage the main trunks. They placed the limbs against the side that faced the shore as well as on the upper deck.

Meanwhile, Spear was gathering driftwood from the shoreline, which he used to build a small fire on the Timer's south side, shielding it from the route to the north.

As the kindling caught fire, Spear turned to Ellie. "This will make little." He then shook his head and made a hand sign.

Ellie laughed. "Smoke!"

With a smile on his handsome face, Spear replied, "Smoke."

Giving him a pat of approval on the shoulder, she spoke to the others, "In the beginning, it was hand signs over half the time. Now, it's only with seldom-used words?"

The others agreed. Soon, they dined on a spread of canned corned beef, salmon on crackers, and canned applesauce. They drank water directly from the lake with varying degrees of concern. True to form, Ellie was very concerned while Bob wasn't concerned at all. They all thought the meal excellent and were glad they had saved some of their best provisions, thanks to the many fish they had caught. Their fishing time had recently been limited though, so they were once again depleting supplies.

A breeze from the north seemed to be keeping mosquitoes away as they sat around their small fire. The group spent this time gazing at the stars and speaking in low voices. More and more, Spear joined in the conversation. Using Ellie's translation skills, he told them many of the stories of the stars and how the legends had named them.

Paul pointed skyward. "Is it any wonder ancient people really kept up with the heavens? Before television, they had plenty of time to follow the movements of the planets and stars. Also, they had no city lights and, thus, were given a great show every clear night."

"They navigated by them, used them in their religions, set their calendars by them, and all sorts of things," said Ellie as she lay back with her head resting on her rolled-up sleeping bag.

"Did you know the stars that make up the front of the bowl of the Big Dipper point down at the North Star? Did you know the North Star is the last star in the handle of the Little Dipper? Spear may not call them by the same names, but I bet he knows," said Bob.

"Put out the fire!" said William with a sharp and urgent tone in his voice.

They quickly extinguished the fire with dirt. The others now stared in the direction demanding William's attention. Four to five miles north, they could see a bright light swinging back and forth across the surface of the lake. It was obviously a spotlight on the enemy ship. Thankfully, the light and enemy craft continued in an easterly direction, leading them to believe they had not been spotted. Within fifteen minutes, the light faded away into the distance.

"How do you think they are finding us now?" asked Paul.

William was quiet for a few seconds and then answered, "I don't think they know where we are. I'll bet when they found the metal ring they had put on Spear, they decided to go in the opposite direction. When they got to the Yellowstone, they probably followed it just like we did."

"Now what do we do?" asked Ellie.

"I think they will assume when we hit the lake, we went due east. I have a surprise in store for them. In the morning, I'll show you what I've been thinking about."

"I have seen you poring over the maps a lot lately," said Bob.

"I have an end run in mind. It takes us south through the Teton Wilderness area before we head back up north to Montana. It's farther, but it should put many miles between us and our friends in the other timer. Let me study it a little more to make sure I know what I'm talking about. I want to be positive we all agree it's the best course."

Everyone was up early the next morning just as the sun peeped over the Absaroka Mountains. William spread his map on the ground and showed the team his prospective route. All agreed it seemed to be a sound plan.

Paul lifted the Timer and headed south over the vast lake. The morning was cool, and a fine mist hung over the water. William leaned over to Paul and told him to fly southeast. They were looking for the Molly Islands.

In a few minutes, they saw a small group of islands in the distance. William told Paul to circle them; they were looking for the mouth of Yellowstone River and where it entered Yellowstone Lake. As they passed over Molly, they saw hundreds of California gulls and pelicans. Oddly enough, William said this was a major breeding ground for the sea fowl. After passing Molly, they came to a marshy area that Bob said contained the river's mouth; it was just a matter of identifying it. A flock of ducks flew up almost directly under them, startling both the ducks and the Timer's passengers. Next, several moose ran away from their morning breakfast. Apparently, the Timer had also frightened these placid creatures.

"I know exactly how they feel," remarked Bob as he rubbed his hand across his stomach. "Missing breakfast is a cruel thing for anyone."

Ellie dropped down the hatch and returned in a few minutes with her hands and pockets full of breakfast for everyone. She had energy bars and a large bag of M&Ms with peanut centers.

"This is the last of the M&Ms, so you better enjoy them," Ellie said as she poured a generous portion into Spear's hand.

Spear held up a red one and placed it in his mouth. Ellie made a biting motion clamping her teeth together, and he followed suit. A broad smile broke out on his face as he crunched through the chocolate shell into the peanut and chocolate center. He looked at Bob, rubbed his stomach, and joined the others in a hearty laugh.

With everyone's assistance, Paul searched over the marshy area for the Yellowstone River's main channel. Bob said that he and William had canoed this area many times and that it wasn't hard going from the river to the lake, but it was difficult going from the lake to the river.

"If the Timer could fly thirty feet high, we could spot the right channel immediately," William said, shaking his head sadly.

Moving inland, they finally found the river's main channel. Paul centered the Timer over the river, and they followed every twist and turn as it led them southward. The river wound back and forth, first heading east then turning west for a while.

William sat quietly, studying a map. "Paul, be on the lookout for a branch heading off to the right."

They soon came to a fork, and Paul drove the Timer down the branch William had described.

After a few minutes, William looked around and said, "I think we've taken a wrong turn. The land should be flattening out by now. Let's turn around, Paul. I think I've given you bad directions. I believe we're on Cliff Creek. We should have come to more forks by now."

Paul eased the Timer around in a tight circle and soon covered the distance back to the main channel. He traveled back up the Yellowstone until William directed him to the next channel on the right.

"Okay, now we watch for forks to the left."

At the second fork to the left, William directed Paul to turn up the stream.

"I believe this is Thorofare Creek," William said to his brother. "Bob, do you remember anything about this area?"

The creek was wide and shallow; most of its banks consisting of rocks rolled there by the early summer floods. The land they were passing through was forested and flat, with large mountains looming directly in their path.

"William, I sure can't say it's the same place, but it looks like where we waded the river hiking to that Yellowstone ranger station."

"Right, I think it is. In about a hundred years, the ranger station and barn will be over there about a mile to the east."

Nodding his head in agreement, Bob responded, "It sure looks different now than when we came through here. That area over to the right was burned over, and a new stand of trees was coming up."

"I remember," replied William. "I also remember the ground was littered with dozens of pieces of petrified rock. You could even see the growth rings on some of them. I bet if you look at those real white stones over there on that bank, they'll be petrified wood."

"Trident Plateau is in that direction, and Thorofare Plateau is over there. They look about the same," William said as he pointed first to the left and then to the right.

They continued up the creek for another mile, rounding a bend in the river. Paul slowed down and then stopped. Ahead, a huge pile of trees and logs were twisted together and stacked at least twenty feet in the air. The log jam extended high into the trees on either side of the river.

Paul looked around. "What do we do now?" he asked in a hushed tone.

Bob leaned on the railing. "Too high to go over, too wide to go around. This is a problem."

"Well, we don't want to cut any more trees if we can avoid it," William said, opening his map and studying it intently. After a minute, he looked up. "I have an alternate plan that just might work. We need to retrace our steps."

Paul again turned the Timer around and started down creek. Where Thorofare entered the Yellowstone, Paul swung the Timer to the left and started back south. They soon approached a fork with a creek trailing off to the southwest. William told Paul to keep going; they were looking for the second creek to the right. At the next fork, Paul turned on this new course and drove down the creek.

Scratching his head, William said, "I think, I hope, this is Atlantic Creek."

This way differed from their previous watercourse as it was a much smaller streambed. They had to maneuver around fallen trees, over small waterfalls, and through tight places. Regardless, their luck remained good, and each time they seemed to find an effective way to continue. The Timer was able to make decent progress the rest of the morning and into the early afternoon. At last, the creek entered a long, open meadow which was a riot of colorful of flowers of all shades blooming in a veritable rainbow of blossoms. They continued to follow the creek down the meadow and watched it disappear into the forest.

"Stay straight, Paul. We should run into Pacific Creek in a minute," instructed William.

Soon, another creek entered the meadow heading to the southwest. Paul drove toward the new creek.

"Would you believe we just crossed the Continental Divide?" asked Bob.

Turning his head, Paul said, "I thought the Continental Divide followed the mountains?"

"Usually, but right here, it crosses this meadow."

"For real?"

"For real. It meanders across this meadow and into the forest on the other side."

Automatically, Paul steered to the center of the new creek as it flowed down the meadow and entered the forest. Here he had to start dodging trees and other obstacles nature had cast in their path.

William looked at his friends. "This is Pacific Creek we're on now. If we had driven into the forest where Pacific entered the meadow, you would have seen the famous 'Parting of the Waters.'"

"The parting of what?" asked Ellie.

"Parting of the Waters. At that point, it becomes Atlantic Creek and Pacific Creek. The waters of Atlantic head east, and Pacific's flows west."

"You're kidding!" said Ellie.

Bob smiled. "No he's not. Two ocean creek divides right on the Continental Divide."

Shaking her head in disbelief, Ellie asked, "So the old story of a fish being able to swim in from the Pacific, cross the country, and end up in the Atlantic is true?"

"If that fish could follow the rivers and streams to Parting of the Waters, yes, it's possible." Bob laughed.

Paul drove down drops, over trees, and pushed his way through limbs, but he made steady progress to the southwest. William said that the Snake River was to be their turning point to head east.

Late that afternoon, the land flattened, and the jagged peaks of the mighty Teton Mountain Range reared up almost directly in front of them. To the south, they could finally see the Snake River's gleam.

"Paul, get us to the river. When we get there, turn east and look for a good place to camp. It's been a long day," said William.

Bob clapped his hands. "We can build a real fire tonight. Spear and I are going to catch some trout and cook them for supper."

Paul soon found a glade near the river and lowered the Timer to the ground. Bob and Spear grabbed their fishing gear and walked to the riverbank. Spear had been an adept student and Bob a good teacher. They had been surprised how little the Plains Indians knew about fishing. William said their fishing mainly consisted of nets called weirs stretched across streams. William and Paul dug through their supplies for something to go with the hoped-for fish. Lastly, Ellie gathered wood and built a fire using the new skills Spear had taught her. This included Spear's lighter.

Shortly, Bob and Spear returned with a string of fat trout. They were cleaned, skewered, and placed over the fire. William and Paul included the meal items they discovered in their search through supplies. The contents of their pantry were dwindling rapidly. Soon sizzling sounds and the delectable smell of roasting trout filled the air.

The trout were delicious, and they finished the meal with the last of the chocolate pudding. Spear told Ellie he loved all sweets but especially chocolate. He had never been exposed to sweets of any kind before meeting them. After he had eaten his pudding, Ellie handed Spear a toothbrush and walked with him to the riverbank. Ellie made sure he brushed his teeth every day. She wanted him to keep his beautiful set of bright, white teeth. As she did this, it reminded her of a problem she had been meaning to mention.

"Does anyone have any extra toothpaste?"

Looks were exchanged between the friends, and finally, Bob said, "To tell you the truth, I've been rationing mine and brushing once a day."

Looking around, Ellie saw a general nodding of heads. "Well, what do we do? I guess we can brush with water."

"Let me do a little looking around," Paul said as he climbed the Timer's ladder and went inside.

After a few minutes, he climbed from the Timer holding two objects in his hands.

"What you got?" asked Bob.

"How about some baking soda and salt?" He held out the two containers and said, "Here is our toothpaste."

"You are kidding!" responded Bob.

"Nope, not quite as tasty as toothpaste, but I think it will work just fine."

"What are we doing with baking soda anyway?" inquired Bob.

Ellie giggled. "Well, I was going to make biscuits, but we've used all the flour for desserts."

"Flour well-spent," said Bob with a knowing look.

After dinner, they sat around the fire and watched the sun set behind the craggy Tetons. The mountains looked like sharp, black teeth painted on the sky's red background.

"That is why I come to these mountains, that scene right there," said William. "It's hard to find sunsets like that back east."

After sitting and talking for a while, the fire began to die down, the cool night began to take hold, and everyone headed for their sleeping bag. The nights were getting colder, and it had been a long day.

They had the usual oatmeal with raisins and brown sugar, and Ellie mentioned they were getting low on the sugar. Bob took this news especially hard, even harder than Spear. They had stretched their stock of food items about as far as it would go, but staples like sugar, flour, salt, pepper, and coffee were impossible to replace.

"I can remember getting used to black coffee pretty fast when we volunteered with the Forest Service. I guess I can do it again," Bob said with a resigned expression.

"You may have to get used to no coffee. I have a bad feeling that will be much worse," said his brother.

William had again spread out his map and was busily going over potential routes. "We'll be coming to the Buffalo Fork River pretty quickly, and a decision needs to be made when we do. I think we need to follow the Buffalo as far as we can then the South Buffalo as far to the east as we can. Anyone have objections or a better idea?" There were no objections or better ideas.

William folded his map and followed the others up the ladder to their seats on top of the Timer. "It may not be easy, but I think it's our best bet," he said.

Following William's instructions, Paul flew them up the Snake River then up the Buffalo Fork. The Buffalo wound through floral meadows filled with an abundance of wildlife. Three times they chased moose out of the river's shallows, across meadows, and into the forest. Someone remarked they had sure passed a lot of moose. They also noted no consistency in how the animals reacted to their presence. They could also see numerous elk and bison off in the distance. Occasionally, they saw mule deer, some with stupendous antlers.

After traveling for several hours, they passed places where Bob and William thought modern dude ranches would be located. They agreed on the future location of Blackrock Ranger Station. This was where the two brothers had volunteered with the Forest Service in previous summers.

This and the next several days were long but wonderfully relaxing. Their only problems were seeking solutions to maneuvering the Timer through or around tight places on the river. It was a nice change not having to worry about the rival timer and its evil crew.

On the third day, they crossed from the Buffalo to the South Buffalo, passed South Fork Falls, and continued to the headwaters. Ellie remarked more than once how beautiful the country was that they were passing through. Low and slow once again came into the conversation and the similarities with riding a horse. To this, Bob added, "A little higher and no saddle sores."

To the surprise of all but Ellie, Spear said he could ride all day and experience no discomfort. He didn't use the word "discomfort," but everyone knew his meaning, and everyone was very impressed.

The following day, as they cruised along without a care in the world, Paul suddenly swerved the Timer into the trees along the south bank of the river. This threw everyone off balance, but it also concealed the Timer in the foliage.

With some difficulty, Paul dropped the Timer through the lower branches and settled it on the ground. Turning to the others, he placed his right index finger to his lips and pointed out into a vast meadow bordering the river. Through the trees, they saw at least twenty horsemen proceeding to the west. Fortunately, their backs were turned away from the river, and they had not seen the Timer or its crew.

CHAPTER 28

A NEW FOE

Spear got a stern look on his face and spoke a word only Ellie understood.

"He said Blackfeet!" she alarmingly reported.

"What are Blackfeet doing this far east?" asked William.

Ellie repeated this question to Spear. With a worried look on his face, he offered her a quick reply.

"Raiding party for horses," she said.

Everyone held their breath as the riders passed over a distant hill and descended into the forest beyond. The Blackfeet were known as superb horse thieves and fearless warriors, and the crew wanted no part of them. William suggested they wait half an hour to make sure there was no further sign of them. After the wait, Paul started up the Timer, raised it off the forest floor, and resumed steering it up the middle of the river.

"I bet they're heading for the Thorofare and then on to Yellowstone," said Bob to his brother.

"What's the Thorofare?" Ellie asked Bob.

"The Thorofare is a wide valley that offers a way through the Absaroka Mountains into Yellowstone. There are several other ways you can do it, but the Thorofare is by far the easiest and best known."

The river was becoming narrower and more difficult for the Timer to traverse. Paul had to make more frequent stops to determine the best route. He would let some of the crew scout ahead for ways around whatever obstacle currently confronted them. Finally, the Timer was no longer able to proceed any further up the riverbed. Paul had to drive the Timer up the riverbank and into the forest. He tried to steer parallel to the river by means of meadows and openings in the trees. This was slow and inconvenient even though their compass verified the craft was traveling pretty much in the desired northwest direction.

William had enough. "Paul, next valley that leads due east, let's follow it."

Looking up from his map that included the future Teton Wilderness area, William said, "This is just too slow and too difficult. We need to see if we can find the Shoshone River."

After several more hours of slow going, a valley did indeed veer off leading east. Looking down at his compass, Paul determined it was almost due east. Paul swung the Timer around and started down the valley. For a change, they made easy, steady progress until it was too dark to see. He dropped the Timer into a small clearing in a narrow stand of trees. They began to unload food and equipment.

Even in the summer, when the sun dropped below the mountains, the temperature dropped as well. Bob, William, and Paul began collecting dried wood. Spear made the usual small tepee-shaped pile of twigs, easily starting a fire.

Ellie unpacked various freeze-dried food packets and pieces of cheese sealed in red wax. She was trying to see what food supplies were left in order to make a menu. Using the roaring fire, she soon had water boiling for food.

After supper, William discussed his plans for using the Shoshone River, providing they could find it. He explained how he thought they could follow the Shoshone all the way to Montana. They still had the problem of locating it even though it was clearly shown on William's map. They had discovered that looking for something at ground level was a totally different prospect. Streams appeared as rivers, and rivers appeared as streams. Valleys turned out to be dead ends, which caused time-consuming backtracking. It could be very confusing.

William leaned forward and poked the fire with a long, crooked stick. "We can get back to the Musselshell by other ways, but it will sure take longer. We can try to find our way between the Wild Horse Range and the Bighorns. We can always circle far to the south and pass south of the Bighorns, but neither of those options appeals to me very much."

Bob looked across the fire at his brother. "William, it will be as hard as can be to find our way between those two mountain ranges. If we go south of the Bighorns, it will add hundreds of miles to our distance. I don't think we have any choice."

"I agree."

Ellie climbed into her sleeping bag, yawned, and said, "Then we'll find the Shoshone."

William looked over at Ellie. "With you, the glass is always half full. You're right. We'll find that river no matter what."

From Ellie's sleeping bag came a sleepy "Sure, we will."

Turning to Paul, William said, "You can drive the Timer through a keyhole. We won't give up until we've given it a really good try."

They heard from Ellie's direction. "We'll find that river," she drawled.

"Tell you what, I'll get up early in the morning and climb up the side of the mountain and see if I can see anything that looks like a river," offered Paul.

From another sleeping bag, Bob spoke up, "I'll go with you."

It was still dark the next morning when Paul and Bob began hiking the mile to the nearest mountainside. Climbing in the twilight slowed them down, but after an hour, the two had reached a rapidly steepening upper slope. They were now hundreds of feet above their campsite and had a five-mile-wide view. They were still in the dark and so was the lower slope and land beneath them. The higher they went, the colder it became. They decided they needed a break from the climbing and the cold.

"Let's sit on this boulder and wait till the sun illuminates some of these valleys," Bob said as he and Paul plunged their hands deep into the pockets of their fleece jackets. The sun now glistened off the mountain peaks off to their east.

Soon, the sun had the cliffs across the valley, glowing white as its rays dropped farther and farther into the ravines and canyons below them. Bob and Paul used binoculars to scan north and northeast with careful deliberation.

"Look for mist coming off the water or a glint of sun on the river when the sun gets higher," suggested Bob.

After a few minutes, Paul exclaimed "There!" and pointed his index finger toward a break in the mountains. "Look just to the right of that flattop mountain."

Bob jumped down from the boulder and climbed some higher rocks behind their perch. He lay down on a flat shelf of rock and scanned off to the north in the direction Paul had pointed.

"Paul, I see something gleaming through the trees. Maybe it's the river. At least, I hope it's the river."

"When the sun first hit that area, I saw a flash through the binoculars. I lowered them for a second and couldn't find the spot when I looked again. Then that bright gleam showed up as the sun rose higher," Paul said as he put his hands back in his pockets to warm his chilled fingers.

"You did well. It's lucky we were here when the sun came up. We could have stayed here all day and never noticed it. Those are thick woods between camp and the river," said Bob.

Getting no answer from Paul, Bob lowered his binoculars. Paul was sitting very still and staring off to the northwest.

"Are you okay?" asked Bob.

"Bob, I think we need to get back quick," Paul said as he pointed across the valley.

Bob sat up on his ledge and looked in the direction in which Paul was pointing. Seeing nothing, he raised his binoculars and then saw a frightening sight. A line of horsemen had come out of the distant forest and were slowly making their way down a hill and across a meadow. They were moving toward a rising curl of smoke that could only be coming from one location, their camp.

"Paul, they are less than an hour from our camp. That's probably going to be close to what it would take for us to get there. You are much faster than I am, so beat it back to camp. You can get the Timer and come back this way to get me."

"Are you sure? I hate to leave you behind."

"I'll be fine. Regardless, if our guys don't get away in the Timer, none of us will be okay. Go now and get there as fast as you can," he said with urgency.

Nodding his head in agreement, Paul said, "I'll get there in time. It's mostly downhill from here."

Paul turned and started back down the slope. The last sight Bob had of Paul, he was slipping and sliding through loose talus before disappearing into the forest.

Bob took a final look in Paul's direction and then turned his attention to the Indians who were moving toward his friends. They were closer but fortunately still moving slowly as if they had all the time in the world.

Bob turned and looked back up the mountainside. He had to find a proper place to wait for his friends. He wanted to be where they could easily see him and fly close to his location. It wouldn't do him much good to be seen if they couldn't get to him. He had to find an accessible spot.

Meanwhile down below, the ground leveled out in front of Paul. Once out of the rocks, he had been able to fly down the slope. He now lost the downhill advantage, so he lowered his chin to his chest, tried to lengthen his stride, and maintain a steady pace. The long downhill had enabled him to run a faster than normal pace, and he was now paying for it. His breathing was ragged, and his stride was becoming shorter. He decided to gradually slow down and concentrate on taking the shortest, easiest route back to their camp. This seemed to help, and unknown to him, he began to gain some distance on the riders.

As Paul got closer, he wanted to yell a warning to the crew but knew he would also alert the Indians. It was obvious from their slow, measured pace that they were trying to sneak up on his friends.

William, Ellie, and Spear were sitting around a small fire, each holding a steaming cup of coffee. They were discussing plans for the day and wondering how long it would be before Bob and Paul returned. They got an answer in a hurry.

Paul suddenly burst through the circling line of trees and ran toward them. As they watched, he stumbled slightly and, after righting himself, yelled, "Get aboard! Get aboard!"

As William, Ellie, and Spear looked on quizzically, Paul quickly covered the distance between them. "Indians, get aboard!" he yelled again, finally spurring them into action.

The friends dropped their coffee mugs and began scrambling up the ladder. After letting Ellie and Spear go first, William vaulted up after them. Closing fast, Paul did a great leap and landed on the third rung and quickly climbed through the railing right on William's heels. Paul then dropped into the driver's seat and immediately started the Timer.

Paul drove the Timer toward a small break in the trees. He was almost out of the clearing when they heard the first whoop, indicating they had company. Looking back across the clearing, William saw the leading riders come through the trees. The Indians, seeing their prey escaping, kicked their mounts and rode after them.

The first arrow made a whistling sound as it flew past William and Paul. Paul hunched himself down in the driver's seat, and William lowered himself partially down the ladder into the interior of the Timer. They could all hear arrows pinging ineffectually against the hull.

Peering down into the Timer's interior, Paul said, "We've got to go get Bob."

"Bob! Where is Bob?" yelled William, looking concerned.

"He asked that I leave him on the side of the mountain. He thought I could get here faster and ahead of these Indians."

"He was right but only barely. No pun, but you ran a big risk."

"That was the farthest and fastest I have ever run."

"Spear says they are Blackfeet," said Ellie as she looked up at William.

"I was afraid of that. That raiding party is now a war party. I need to get up where I can see."

Ellie patted William's shoulder. "Well, be careful."

"I will."

William raised his head above the hatch, which caused a flurry of arrows against the hull and over their heads. Their craft was only fifteen feet above the ground and not very far ahead. William crawled through the hatch and flattened himself against the deck.

"Okay, Paul, what can we do to get a lead on these guys?"

Paul had driven them out of the clearing and was now driving wildly through the trees. He knew slowing down or stopping might prove detrimental.

Paul looked over his shoulder to assess their lead. "They may be able to follow us, but I'm not going to make it easy for them. Let's make them work for it."

Paul steered the Timer over a stretch of downed timber that caused their pursuers to slow their horses to a walk. Some others saw a game trail and were able to get through the fallen trees much faster. They now took up the chase. The Timer flew over a deep gully that slowed the riders again. As they flew ahead, Paul and William looked back to see the riders emerge from the gully, resuming their pursuit. The war party had fallen behind but obviously wasn't giving up.

As the Timer pulled ahead, Paul could sit a little higher in his seat and William could grasp the railing and kneel since the onslaught of arrows had waned. They also had a much better view of the upcoming terrain. This allowed them a better choice of obstacles to place before their pursuers.

"I think we need to veer further to the west. I think that's where I left Bob."

Steering up the mountainside, he drove the Timer more to their right; as the threat of being shot with arrows lessen, Ellie and Spear clambered onto the deck to assist in looking for Bob. The steep slope, along with downed timber, rockslides, talus, ravines, and intermittent forest had slowed down their pursuers. At the same time, it made them much easier to see and, thus, to follow.

"We sure can't escape heading in this direction, but we have no choice. We've got to find Bob," said Paul.

"Yeah, I can't leave my brother. I really might miss the big guy," William joked but with a worried look.

With all four sets of eyes scanning the mountain slope, Paul continued driving them on a course several hundred feet up the mountain. Surely, they would spot Bob soon.

"There!" yelled Ellie. She pointed to a spot of blue several hundred yards away and higher than their current position. The spot of blue quickly became a distant figure waving something blue. This distant figure then became Bob standing on top of a pile of boulders energetically waving his blue fleece jacket. There was no mistaking Bob Wattson and his blue jacket.

Paul changed their flight angle and headed directly for Bob. At the same time, a group of riders poured out of a ravine and through a small stretch of woods, now joining in the race.

Suddenly, Spear pointed at the valley ahead. More riders approached from yet another direction. It was going to be a close race. Who would get to Bob first?

The riders in front of them reined in their steeds with much shouting and rearing of horses. They dropped their reins and started on foot up the mountainside toward Bob. They had to move cautiously as the slope was particularly steep. Caution was also necessary to avoid the rocks Bob now began to roll down the mountainside at them.

Paul turned to William, deeply concerned. "William, I don't think we can get that high."

"Paul, do the best you can. We've got to get closer."

Paul drove the Timer toward Bob's perch. Finally, the Timer would go no higher. The slope was just too steep, and there was nothing for the Timer to reflect off and suspend itself. The craft was not going to be able to climb high enough to reach Bob.

Bob seemed to realize the Timer had reached its limit; he was going to have to go to them. Bob began to scramble down the rocks toward his friends. Finally, where the Timer could go, the slope's steepness stopped Bob, and he could go no lower. Paul continued trying to drive toward Bob, but they were just fifteen feet too low.

William cupped his hands and yelled to his brother. "No choice, Bob. Prepare to jump when we get under you. We'll try to get as close as possible to the wall. When you jump, make sure you clear the railing and land on your feet." With that, William reached in a pocket and gripped one of the dark pistols and laid it across his left foreman. He quickly checked the pistol's air pressure charge and its load of darts; both were ready to go.

Paul slowed the Timer twelve to fifteen feet under the boulder where Bob stood. The Timer seemed to sway back and forth as if uncertain being this high. William thought the jump must look much higher to his brother. Finally, Bob gathered his courage and leaped for the deck. At almost the same time, another figure came through an opening in the rocks and hurtled after him. The first things William noticed were three feathers standing straight up from the back of his head and the long, wicked-looking knife he was holding in his right hand.

Bob cleared the railing and crashed onto the deck with knees bent. This seemed to somewhat cushion his landing, but he still landed with a crash. He stumbled forward and finished in a heap against the railing on the far side of the deck.

"Watch out!" yelled William to his brother as a figure landed at Bob's feet, rolled, and then stood above him, holding the cruel knife above his head.

"Duck!" shouted William as he fired his pistol at the Indian standing over his brother. The dart blossomed in the buckskin pants over the right thigh, and he collapsed almost immediately, the knife falling from his hand as he slipped over the side of railing.

Bob quickly reached over and with his right hand grabbed a handful of his buckskin shirt. He held on to the railing with his other hand in a desperate attempt to keep them both from falling down the steep mountainside. William seized his brother's lower leg and held on. With William now stabilizing him, Bob was able to release his left hand from the railing. Grasping the young Indian with both hands, Bob easily lifted him up and over the railing, depositing the limp figure on the Timer's deck. He was about Spear's size, with a long, crooked nose and braids hanging down his back. Paul wheeled the Timer around and headed for the distant river. The Timer gathered speed as it almost skated down the slope. The Blackfeet saw this and ran for their horses.

Bob reached down and snatched the dart out of his attacker's leg. There was a low moan, but he didn't wake up.

"He'll be fine, but we need to make sure we stay fine," William said, his voice serious.

Paul was driving between trees and over downed timber, gullies, and anything else he thought might impede the riders. He steadily gained a lead of a hundred yards when they reached the river. This cushion made them feel much better.

Paul looked over at William. "That's got to be the south fork of the Shoshone River."

"From looking at the map earlier, I don't know what else it could be," William replied. He then told Paul about a strategy he wanted to try. "It might just buy us a bigger lead than the one we have right now," and then he leaned closer and told Paul his idea.

Staying just out of arrow range, Paul drove across the Shoshone.

There he steered the Timer parallel to the bank and started on a course heading to Montana. The Indians splashed in and swam their mounts across the river after them. As soon as the last horse hit dry land and a few arrows flew their way, Paul drove them back across the river to the east bank.

There were war cries and yells of frustration once the Indians realized what Paul was doing. A tall Indian, who they presumed was a chief, began shouting and pointing. Half of the group began swimming their horses back across the river.

By this point, Paul had pulled still farther ahead, and the winded Indian ponies were struggling to keep up. They had been running and swimming for much of the last hour and were tiring fast. Paul had now quit searching for obstacles. He was driving along the river by the fastest, straightest way possible. As Bob liked to say, two of the best things about the Timer were that it didn't eat grass and it didn't get tired.

The river ahead had narrowed into a small canyon. The banks began steepening to become cliffs. This was what the crew had been looking for. As the banks grew higher and closer together, tree branches covered more of the river. Now Paul had to steer out over the center of the water. As their pursuers had no bank to ride on, they reined in their horses. Just then, the Timer rounded a bend, and they lost sight of the trailing Indians for the first time since the original pursuit had started earlier in the day. It was a relief to finally be just the friends. Almost...

"Drop a little lower, Paul. I think it's time for us to turn our captive loose. He hasn't been as nice as Spear," Bob said.

After a quick look at the murderous expression on Spear's face, Bob thought it was lucky for their captive that he and Spear were not alone. Obviously, Spear's tribe and the Blackfeet were not the best of friends.

Paul looked over at Bob and saw him holding the prisoner's arm behind his back. He did not appear to be applying much pressure, just enough to keep him in a sitting position.

Paul lowered the Timer to just above the water's surface. Bob stood up and pulled his adversary with him, gripping him about the waist. In one swift motion, Bob lifted him off his feet, held him at arm's length out over the water, and dropped him. The Blackfoot landed with a huge splash and went under. He immediately surfaced, spitting water and thrashing wildly about.

Clapping his right palm against his forehead, Bob suddenly exclaimed, "That's just great. I don't think he can swim."

"Of course, he can't swim!" yelled Ellie. "Do something, Bob, and do it right now!"

Bob, quickly jerking off his boots, placed one foot up on the railing and, stepping up with the other, dove in. He hit the water cleanly, surfaced, and swam to his former captive. Overpowering the flailing Indian, Bob wrapped an arm around his shoulders and swam one handed toward the bank. When he got in the shallows, Bob pushed the sputtering brave toward some driftwood. The Indian could use it to float back to his companions.

Bob turned and began swimming back to the center of the river. Paul lowered the Timer, and Bob started climbing the ladder.

The young Indian had, by now, reached the riverbank. He walked up to a large pile of rocks, bent over, and selected several flat, smooth ones. The Blackfoot began throwing them at Bob. Two hit the side of the Timer with no effect, but one did strike a glancing blow on Bob's lower leg.

"Ouch! Paul, get me out of here before I go get him and throw him back in the river!"

William leaned down, holding out a hand to his brother. "Remember, no good deed goes unpunished."

Rolling his eyes and shaking water out of his hair, Bob responded, "Yeah, but that was a really extraordinary good deed, particularly since he tried to kill me first."

Casting a skeptical eye toward the bank, he watched as one last rock hurled toward them. This rock clanged against the railing and spun off into the river. Their former prisoner then turned and began making his way south back to his horse.

While the others laughed at Bob, Paul kept the Timer midstream and followed the river north. The river twisted and turned but stayed on a generally north by northwest course the rest of the day. Late that afternoon, the group saw a narrow, sandy beach at the foot of a fifty-foot bluff. They agreed this would be a good place to spend the night.

Bob and Paul found their fishing rods and soon had caught six fat trout, which they cleaned and got ready for cooking. William gathered wood, and Spear had built a fire. Ellie retrieved some salt from the Timer's pantry and mentioned their supply was getting low, eliciting the usual chorus of moans, groans, and "I told you we should bring more salt" from everyone but Spear who watched in amusement.

The trout were skewered on green sticks which had been driven into the ground. After a few minutes, they sizzled and popped as drippings fell onto the fire. Ellie cooked a large pot of freeze-dried beans. While doing so, she prudently reported that this was the last of them.

Soon the fish were placed on a flat, dry piece of driftwood and the pot of beans removed from the fire. As they divided the fish and scooped the beans straight from the pot, they roundly declared the meal a big success.

After supper, William spoke to the group, "Well, it's obvious we need to do a better job of watching out for trouble. Today could have been really bad."

"Do we need to start setting up sentries at night again?" Bob asked William.

"I think it depends on where we are. If we're in a place like this, it's probably not necessary. If we're out on the plains or a more heavily traveled area, probably yes. It can't possibly hurt."

"With five of us, we could do two hours each and cover the whole night. That wouldn't ruin anyone's sleep," suggested Paul.

"It's a good idea, but I don't think it's necessary tonight," William said as the final word on the matter.

The night sky was pitch-black, through which the stars burned with a bright, white luster. It seemed the air was getting a little cooler each night as Wyoming crept closer to autumn. They had endured several more dustings of snow and some cold rain and sleet; however, tonight was almost perfect. They had spread two tarps on the sand and slept soundly in their sleeping bags under the starry sky.

CHAPTER 29

—————————◆—————————

BACK TO MONTANA

BOB WANTED TO catch some fish for breakfast but was overruled the next morning. After a quick meal, they got off to an early start. As usual, Paul steered to the middle of the river and headed north. As the sun rose higher, the river was striped with shadows cast by trees on the bank. The water's surface was occasionally broken by a fish taking low-flying insects, and the day had started off calm and peaceful.

Several hours later, as they sat on the top of the Timer, Ellie looked up from a shirt she was mending. "What is that horrible smell?"

As Spear held his nose, several of the others said, "Rotten eggs!"

"Well, at least I think I know where we are," laughed William.

"Where?" asked Ellie.

"I think we're on the Stinking Water River."

"You're kidding, aren't you?" asked Ellie in a squeaky voice as she pinched her nose.

"Nope, that's what the Shoshone River was called at one time. I think we are about to enter Coulter's Hell near where the town of Cody is going to be."

Swiveling around, Paul asked, "I thought Coulter's Hell is what they called Yellowstone?"

William looked up, "Bob?"

"Actually, historians are unsure whether John Coulter ever even entered Yellowstone. This was the original Coulter's Hell."

Putting a hand on Paul's shoulder, William said, "Drive carefully, we should be entering a volcanically active region of the river soon."

"Is it safe?" asked Ellie in a troubled voice.

"It should be, but I don't know about geysers or hot springs. We should be fine, but just be careful," replied William.

In a few minutes, they rounded a bend in the river and could see steam rising off the banks and water. The odor was stronger but didn't seem to bother them as much.

William leaned with his elbows on the railing. "I'll say this. The river's name sure fits."

"What's causing all the steam?" asked Paul.

"Fumaroles. There is water but not enough to be a geyser. The heat evaporates the water, and steam is expelled," said William, also reminding them of the numerous ones they had seen in Yellowstone.

They continued following the river, and soon, William noted a landmark off to the west. "That's Heart Mountain. We should be only thirty to forty miles from where we meet the Big Horn River."

"How do you know all this?" asked Ellie.

"Dad drove Bob and me all over the states of Wyoming and Montana. The museums at Cody were one of his favorite places. We drove down the road that borders the Shoshone River many times. We know this part of Wyoming pretty well."

As the riverbanks passed by, they saw numerous hot springs flowing into the river, including one from the top of a cone twenty feet high. Several small geysers sprayed water over the river, making the surface appear to dance.

Days were staying light well into the evenings, so the friends decided to continue until they hit the Big Horn River. The miles rolled slowly by with the usual bison, elk, deer, and occasional bear on the banks. They passed a huge mother grizzly and two cubs feeding on an elk kill in a small meadow. She barely raised her head as her two offspring rolled and tumbled over each other in the grass.

Spear tied fishing line to several arrows and tried to shoot fish in the shallows as they flew past. After a dozen attempts, he finally hit a nice trout and pulled it on board. He got several congratulations and pats on the back, responding with "Good, good, good!"

With the sun setting below the mountains, the river merged into another stream coming up from the south. They decided this had to be the Big Horn River heading up to Montana. The craft veered left as their course shifted from east to north.

It was again time to search for a camping spot for the night. Soon, Paul spotted a small clearing just beyond the bank and dropped the Timer onto it. This place was just above a low bank, which looked down on a sandbar. A large tangle of gnarled driftwood was piled against one end of the sandbar. They collected some of it and soon had a roaring fire going. William thought the fire would not be visible because the sandbar was well below the top of the bank and was also built in a hastily dug shallow pit. Shielding trees also dotted both banks.

They finished eating and were sitting around their fire, poking at it with sticks, when William spoke up, "I want to go a few more miles on the Big Horn and then drive across country. This will put us a little west of our destination, but there is something I want to see." When asked about the mystery location, he merely replied, "Wait and see."

They unrolled their sleeping bags and turned in as it had been a long day. Each wore a sock cap at night due to now-cooler evenings. Their sleeping bags were warm enough, but heads sticking out of the bags got cold. Ellie was the only one who had a mummy bag with built-on hood. Being warm just seemed to make for a more comfortable night's sleep.

The next morning, after a sparse breakfast of energy bars, they started up the Bighorn. Bob said the supply depletion was really getting to him and pointed out that even his cache of candy bars was gone.

After an hour, William told Paul to find a good spot to exit the river. Paul found a low, sloping bank and drove the Timer up the bank and out onto the plains.

Shielding his eyes from the early morning sun, William said, "Paul, put our heading due north." The mystery continued as he still refused to say where they were going.

Shortly after starting across the great expanse, Ellie spoke up, "What in the world is that?" She pointed to the northeast at what appeared to be a huge, black snake winding its way through the sky toward them. They all looked at the strange sight, but none could offer an explanation as to what it was.

"Drive on, Paul," William said. "It's going to pass right in front of us if we hurry. We need to get closer."

"William, I think I know what it may be," said his brother.

"What?" was William's puzzled reply.

"Birds."

"Birds?" both Ellie and Paul said at the same time with a look of incongruity on their faces.

"I think it may be passenger pigeons."

"You know, I bet you're right. They were still around in the early 1800s," said William.

"They were around a lot later than that," Bob added.

Following William's direction, Paul increased speed as they wanted to make sure they didn't miss this awesome sight. They soon found out there was no danger of that. The spectacle greeting them as they got closer was startling in scope. The almost-solid mass of birds was over a mile wide, and their numbers, unimaginable, extended off to the north as far as they could see. They blotted out the sun, and a dark shadow followed beneath the flock as it weaved across the prairie. Getting even closer, they found the enormity of the mass staggering. As Paul stopped just short of their projected path, they heard a whirring sound. The group sat there open-mouthed as the birds just kept on coming. Now using their binoculars, the friends could see many of the birds were gray with red breasts.

"They kind of look like robins, but they're passenger pigeons for sure. How in the world did these birds go extinct with numbers like this?" asked William.

"People!" replied Ellie irritably.

"Ellie's right," Bob said. "They were killed in nesting colonies in numbers we can't comprehend. There was one colony where fifty thousand birds were killed each day for three months."

"Wow, that doesn't seem possible," responded Ellie.

"Even being killed in those numbers, there sure are a lot of them here today," said William.

They watched the flock pass over for hours, and there appeared no end to them. Now, the tightly packed birds extended out of sight in both directions. The crew watched in silence, each contemplating that no one in their lifetime would ever see such a sight. They also knew you had to see it to believe and appreciate it even though they had taken many photos.

William shook his head. "What man did to the animals of this country is almost impossible to believe. We wiped out this magnificent species of bird, and the same thing nearly happened to the buffalo. We almost killed off both at the same time."

"Only the remoteness of Yellowstone saved the buffalo, and it was still too close for comfort," added Bob.

"How was that?" asked Paul softly as if he didn't want to startle the flock.

"Almost all the great herds were killed off, and extinction was a real possibility. Then they found about fifty in Yellowstone. Yellowstone had been too difficult, in terms of weather and seclusion, to make it worthwhile for the hunters. Those fifty were bred with others from private ranches, and the breed was saved."

William lay back on the Timer's deck, propping his feet on the railing. Putting his hands behind his head, he stared up at the passenger pigeons and said, "Samuel de Champlain was a French explorer who described passenger pigeons in terms of countless numbers. Others used the word 'multitudes,' yet in a few years, they'll all be gone."

"You would think it would have taken some kind of epidemic to do that," said Bob.

Shaking his head, William said, "It did an epidemic of killing." He sat up. "These were the most social of birds. When hundreds would get in trees, they would perch on one another. Their weight would break the branches. It is said, during this time, there may have been five billion."

"Is that billion with a 'b'?" asked Paul.

"Yes. It has been speculated that as many as a third of the birds in the United States were passenger pigeons. One huge flock was estimated at one hundred and thirty-six million."

"How could you even count a hundred million?" asked Ellie.

"I don't know," William said. "I presume that's where the word 'estimate' comes into play."

Pointing to the sky, Paul said, "You can bet this flock would be counted in the millions."

The others nodded in agreement. The numbers to create such a sight defied imagination. Getting in the driver's seat, Paul decided to take them a little closer. As they approached, the whirring sound became louder and louder.

"I don't believe I would get any closer if I were you, Paul," William said.

"Why is that?"

"What happens when you wash your car and park it outside?"

"Do you mean something that would cause me to wash it again and you don't mean rain?"

"That's exactly what I mean."

CHAPTER 30

———————————◆———————————

PIONEER LANDMARK

THE FRIENDS WATCHED the flock for another hour, making for a total of seven hours. Unbelievably, the stream of passenger pigeons continued with no end in sight. Paul started the Timer and headed north. They had witnessed a spectacle they would never forget. The film and photos they had taken would not do it justice.

As they moved to the north, William guessed they had forty to fifty miles to go. The crew badgered him continually about where they were headed. Finally giving in, he told them he wanted to see Pompey's Pillar. This was a huge sandstone formation rising out of the prairie that became a landmark for the settlers moving west. After traveling across hundreds of miles of featureless plains, it seemed to offer hope they were making progress toward their destination.

"What Roman senator was it named after?" asked Bob with a laugh.

Returning the laughter, William replied, "Believe it or not, it was not named after a Roman senator. It was named after Sacagawea's son. William Clark had given him the nickname 'Pomp.'" He turned to face his brother. "He had originally named it 'Pompey's Tower,' but the editor of their journals changed the name to Pompey's Pillar. The Indians called it 'the place where the mountain lion lies.' Take your choice."

After several more hours of flying, they saw, in the distance, the jutting presence of Pompey's Pillar. It took another two hours to reach it, but they all agreed it was worth the detour. Just north of their location, they could see a river, which William said would be the Yellowstone.

"The next time I see the Yellowstone River, I want to follow it back into the part of Yellowstone we missed this time," Bob said. The others agreed.

Looking up at the formation, Paul said, "It must be a hundred feet high."

"More like one hundred and fifty feet," corrected William.

Paul drove the Timer under a tree on the south side of the huge formation. They dropped the required gear to the ground and began settling in for the night. They decided against a fire because it would probably be visible for miles out here.

"I think we need to post sentries tonight," William said, a solemn tone in his voice.

The others agreed it would be foolhardy not to do so; better safe than sorry. They decided to have the first lookout begin at eight for a two-hour shift. They spotted a nice ledge above the Timer that would serve as a good lookout perch for the sentry.

Poking Paul on the shoulder, Bob suggested they go look for William Clark's famous carving on the Pillar of W. CLARK, JULY 25, 1806. Paul agreed, and they stood up to start the search.

Then William pointed out, "We are in 1805. William Clark hasn't carved it yet. He carved it on the way back to the east."

"Gosh, it's hard to keep this time thing straight," Paul said as he rubbed the back of his hand across his forehead.

William said they were probably the first people in over one hundred and seventy-five years who wanted to see the carving and couldn't.

After a cold supper, Ellie took the first lookout shift. She moved easily up the rocks and settled in twenty-five feet above the Timer. Calling down, she said, "You can see much better and much farther from up here."

Spear took the second shift and was followed by Bob, William, and finally Paul.

Dawn was breaking as Paul finished his turn. He had seen nothing of interest during the night but a small buffalo herd ambling by. He stood scanning off to the west with his binoculars. Hearing some scrambling sounds, he looked down to see William ascending to his ledge. As he stepped up next to him, Paul placed his binoculars down on the rock and stretched. William sat down next to Paul and hugged his knees as he leaned back against the wall.

"Seen anything?"

"Nope, nothing. Although it's only been in the last few minutes you could see very far."

William reached over and picked up Paul's binoculars, and, adjusting them, he propped his elbows on a rock and slowly began to move them across the rapidly brightening horizon. He did this for a few minutes with no results. Putting down the binoculars, he rubbed his eyes and sat quietly, resting them for a minute. Again, he took up the binoculars and began sweeping the country out to the west. As he moved from left to right, he paused and then shifted his gaze back over a spot he had already covered. Paul saw him draw in his breath and fix on a spot far out to the west.

"Do you see something, William?'

"I'm not sure. There's a mist coming off the river, but I think I saw some movement. It's a longways off, so maybe I'm seeing things. I hope so anyway."

"Things do tend to jump around when you're looking at them from a long distance. It's hard to stay focused on one spot."

"Well, let me keep looking. I'm trying to watch some of the openings in the trees lining the river. I think I'm looking ahead of where I might have seen movement, but I'm not really sure."

"William, do you want me to get the spotting scope and come up here and help you?"

"That might not be a bad idea. It can't hurt to have another set of eyes looking over this big country." Staring hard through the binoculars, William suddenly blurted out, "Wait a minute, wait just a minute...Paul, go get the Timer warmed up and wake up the others. I'll be right behind you. It's the other timer. It's following the Yellowstone!"

They slid down, in a shower of rocks, to the Timer. Paul jumped into the driver's seat, and William leaned down through the hatch. "Everyone wake up! We've got company!"

William straightened up and turned to Paul. "Keep us as low as possible, Paul. Maybe we can find a place to hide. This wide-open prairie doesn't offer many possibilities."

"William, maybe I can keep this rock formation between us and the other timer."

"The problem would be if they saw us, we'd be really close. They would catch us for sure. No, Paul, drive us out over the river. It's got lots of twists and turns. Maybe they won't be able to see too far ahead for a while."

"That makes sense to me. If we stay out here in this open country, they will see us for sure."

William put his hand on his friend's shoulder. "It may work for the time being, but their faster speed will overtake us before too many miles."

Coming up from below, Bob leaned in. "At least it'll give us a little time to think of something to do."

Paul drove them to the Yellowstone through an opening in the trees and then out over the water. He headed down river as fast as the Timer would go. The bends in the river kept them out of view of the enemy timer for the next hour. Then they came to a long, straight stretch. It was going to be impossible to get to the next turn without being seen.

"We've got to turn north at some point to get to our departure location. Should we try it now?" Bob asked, glancing back over his shoulder.

William shook his head. "I just don't know. We can't afford to get caught, and I just don't think in a race we can get there ahead of them."

Keeping the Timer flying straight down the river, Paul waited for suggestions, but there were no ideas forthcoming. In only a few minutes more, it was readily apparent the other timer had spotted them. Looking back through the spotting scope, Bob reported much arm waving and finger pointing in their direction. They were only four to five miles ahead, and Paul was pushing the Timer as fast as it would go.

Another thirty minutes passed, and the distance between the two timers rapidly decreased. "Paul, find a low place and get us off the river," said William, worry showing on his face.

In a few minutes, Paul found a low section of the north bank and wheeled the Timer off the river, up the bank, and out on the plains. "At least this will give us more room to maneuver," he said. It seemed the best hope they had.

Suddenly, Spear stood up, slightly flexing his knees against the movement of the Timer. He stood quietly for a second and then pointed off to the north. "Look there, buff-a-lo is coming."

Looking to the north, they could see in the distance a huge dust cloud moving toward them. Now they were aware of a deep, distant rumbling. It was as though they were hearing thunder from a long way off. It was very indistinct, but it was there.

"Head toward them, Paul," directed William. "They may save us yet."

Paul turned the Timer just a little more to the northeast and drove toward the dust cloud. Looking behind them, Bob saw the other timer turn to match their course. It drew closer and closer.

Soon, the sound of distant thunder became a continuous roar as they approached the large herd. It had changed from a dust cloud to a reddish-brown moving mass to individual animals. The ground seemed to quiver and undulate below them. Over a low rise came the lead animals. It was like the tip of a spear. The herd spread out in a triangular shape, the lead buffalo being the point of the triangle which quickly broadened to hundreds of yards in width. As they watched, it broadened by the minute. Soon the leaders were gone, but the river of animals continued to flow past their vantage point.

The Timer entered the edge of the dust cloud. It was as if someone drew a semitransparent screen down in front of their eyes.

Sensing the coming problem, Ellie shouted above the tumult, "Quick, Bob. Get Paul some night-vision glasses. They may not help him see any better, but maybe they'll keep the dust out of his eyes."

"Get me a pair as well, Bob," William said anxiously. "And some towels."

Bob quickly dropped down the hatch and returned in a moment with two sets of night-vision glasses.

It seemed strange to ride toward the immense buffalo herd so low to the ground. It was almost as if they would crash into them. The other timer was now only a quarter mile behind, and they could see men gathering on their deck carrying guns.

As the Timer approached the herd's edge, they could see flashes from the guns, but the sound of the stampeding buffalo was so great that they could hear nothing else. They felt the faint vibration of shells hitting their hull but could hear none of the pings and clangs that were typically made. Verbal communication was impossible, so William quickly motioned everyone but Paul to move below deck. There was no argument from anyone as the dust quickly became blinding and breathing was difficult.

Bob reappeared from below and handed caps and towels to William and Paul. The pair pulled the caps down low on their brows and tied the towels securely across their lower faces. Bob, seeing his brother and friend were equipped as well as possible, dropped down inside, closing the hatch cover behind him.

The Timer was only ten feet above the heaving, leaping animals that carpeted the ground as far as they could see. The farther into the herd they flew, the thicker the dust became. After what they guessed was a half mile, only a short distance could be seen in any direction. One thing about that: if they couldn't see out, the other timer couldn't see in. The only thing permitting them to stay on course was their compass. Paul had to continually wipe it with his hand in order to read it.

William leaned into Paul, taking a swift glance at the compass. Motioning with his hand, he had Paul turn the Timer to a straight-north setting. Steering to this new direction, Paul now had the Timer flying directly over the streaming animals. The sensation was like riding a boat over a river that plunged directly under the front of your vessel. William, straightening his arm next to Paul's head, waved it up and down, indicating Paul to stay on that course.

Leaning against the back of Paul's seat, William thought of a way that might allow them to escape their pursuers. There was certainly nothing to lose by giving it a try. Rather than pass through the herd to the other side, William decided to stay above the herd for as long as possible. He had no idea how long that might be, but he felt the enemy timer probably couldn't find them in this huge dust cloud.

Finding a third towel Bob had placed on the deck, he periodically wiped the dust from their glasses, which were being coated rapidly. This would help for a few minutes and then had to be repeated. This continued for miles. Like the passenger pigeons, the numbers were almost beyond belief. After approximately two hours, the herd passing beneath them began to thin out. There appeared gaps in the solid mass of animals, and the dust began to settle.

Finally, when the dust was reduced to a less choking haze, William tapped on the hatch, which opened, and Bob peeked out through a crack. Bob, Ellie, and Spear quickly climbed out and stood in the six inches of dust deposited on the deck.

Looking over at William and Paul, they pointed and then laughed until they were gasping for breath. William and Paul were caked with dust from head to foot. The Timer's upper deck had so many layers of dust that it was leaving its own trail, billowing behind them.

William and Paul removed their glasses, masks, and caps and breathed big sighs of relief. There was dust up their sleeves and pants legs down the front of their shirts and in their boots. William waved his arms, and Paul jumped up and down. Clouds of dust billowed from their clothes, and their friends pleaded with them to settle down.

William took both hands and ran them through his now darkened hair, and again, dust flew everywhere. Paul sat with his back against the railing, pouring dust out of his boots.

"I feel filthy!" said William, looking disgusted.

"Me as well!" Paul replied. "What I would give for a hot shower about now."

CHAPTER 31

CAUGHT OR ESCAPE AGAIN?

"So far, so good," Ellie said as she scanned in all directions with their spotting scope. "I don't see those guys anywhere, and I'm glad of it."

"Keep looking," William said. "They're out there somewhere, and we don't want them slipping up on us."

"Will do."

Putting his hands on his hips and looking westward, William said, "Let's get the trackers working and see if we can home in on the beacons." Now, looking back over his shoulder, he said, "We really don't know what the other timer did or where it is right now. We just know it's not here and that we better get moving."

"I doubt they or anyone else would be as crazy as you two to stay outside in all that dust and drive through it," Bob said, amused. The others laughed.

Bob and Ellie went below, returning with two tripods topped with black, rectangular, metal boxes. These boxes each had an antenna projecting up from the top and red and green buttons at one end. In the center of the top was a round glass dial.

"Let's turn one on and save the other," Bob said to his brother.

"Okay by me."

Sweeping with the sides of their boots, they cleared away an area of the several inches of accumulated dust and set up one of the tripods. Bob leaned over down and pushed the green button. The button lit up with a low, humming sound. Now, the box began to rotate. After a minute, it stopped and appeared to lock on a set direction. The humming gradually became louder and steady.

"Paul, steer the Timer in that direction and watch what happens. Now, steer a few degrees to the south," William instructed.

Paul turned a little to the left. The humming sound dropped in volume. The farther he steered to the left, the lower the volume and the less steady the humming. Finally, it was almost impossible to hear any sound.

William smiled. "Back to the west."

Paul steered back to the right, and the humming immediately became louder. Going a little to the right of the proper angle caused the sound to drop and the humming to lessen. He made another slight correction, and the sound increased and steadied, indicating they were on the right course. Paul put their flight direction on the rudimentary automatic pilot, and they proceeded west.

Now Paul and William happily went below and changed their jumpsuits. They brought their dust-covered ones up top and hung them on the railing to air out. This caused such a cloud of dust that the others made them shift their clothes to the back rail as everyone had been getting dust in their eyes.

Bob leaned back against the left side railing. "I say let's go 'til we get to the beacons. I would really like some milk, ice cream, eggs, and bread."

William spoke up, "So would the rest of us, especially the ice cream." He looked at Spear. "Wait until you taste ice cream."

"Ice cream?" said Spear, looking puzzled.

"You will like it!" William said.

The sun was setting, lighting up the western horizon with a black edge and a multicolored but predominately red, sky. Bob stared at it. "I do miss certain foods like ice cream, but I'm really going to miss this too." The others agreed.

As the Timer flew west, the crew watched the sunset followed by the darkening of the sky. A light snow drifted down and began coating the Timer and the crew. Warm jackets and caps were passed up from below, and everyone wrapped up against the cold.

William suggested they get the nightscopes out as a precaution against being surprised by the other timer. The crew constantly scanned forward for obstacles and to the rear for pursuers. They could see neither and proceeded on through the night.

No one slept that night because they were all too excited about getting home. Everyone stayed on the upper deck, heedless of the cold night air rushing across the Timer's top. At least it was ridding the Timer of some dust. The snow had finally stopped but not before coating everyone and everything, including the remaining dust in every crack and crevice. The sky remained dark and low as they traveled at less than full speed. With neither stars nor moon, the night was pitch-black. They were glad to be steered by the steady hum of the tracker and not that of visual aids as there were none to be had. The nightscopes helped but only to a limited degree. Flying across vast, treeless plains helped as well.

After a long night, the friends could see a thin edge of light visible on the eastern horizon. It did not burn away the gloom, but it definitely improved their ability to see the surroundings.

Bob crawled over to the tracker on the icy deck as the Timer's forward movement made upright walking an adventure. He wiped away the snow and some caked dust from the glass dial. Ellie slid over to him and peered over his shoulder. The dial was lit and had three circular rings on its face. There was also a blinking dot at the outside edge of the screen. As Ellie watched, the blinking dot slowly moved toward the dial's center.

"I have an idea of what I'm looking at, but explain it a little more," she said.

"The rings are set at twenty kilometers, ten kilometers, and one kilometer from the beacons. Dailey said it works really well, and only the last half mile or so is tricky."

With a smile, Ellie replied, "I would think that's the most important half mile?"

"It is. It's just a matter of getting close and then searching out the beacons."

The humming stayed constant, and the blinking dot passed through the first ring and then the second. They were now six tenths of a mile from home. William joined them and now was also watching the dial and their progress toward the beacons.

"Slow and steady as you go, Paul," William said, his face inches from the dial.

"Okay."

Finally, William said, "Stop. As best as I can tell, we're at the center. I repeat, as best as I can tell."

Paul slowly brought the Timer to a halt and lowered the craft to only a few feet off the ground. "Now what?" he asked.

"Spear doesn't know what to look for, so he stays on the Timer with you. Bob, Ellie, and I will get on the ground and search until we find the beacons." Looking at his brother and Ellie, William said, "Let's stagger ourselves out every ten feet and search in a circle from the Timer. If we don't find it in the first circuit, we move out to the last person and start again."

"Sounds good to me. We'll see how good you are at finding the grid's center," Bob said.

"Thanks, I think. I'm not sure that shows much confidence in me, but I'll take it."

The three climbed to the ground and began spacing themselves, circling around the Timer. It was slow going, but they didn't want to miss the metal rods and their way home.

"There ought to be a better way than this. If we come back, we need to mark the spot so it's easier to find. Maybe tie a ribbon or a piece of cloth to the bush," William speculated.

Bob bent at the waist to look at a bush then looked over at his brother. "Just remember, if it's easier for us to find, it might make it easier to call someone else's attention to them. We would have to be very, very careful."

"I agree."

Finally, after their third circle, Ellie cried out, "Over here, I found one!"

"Great!" William replied happily. "Stand right there, Ellie. Now we'll search off you. It shouldn't be difficult."

Bob and William walked over to Ellie and, using her as a guide, quickly found the second beacon. Instructing Bob to stand at the second beacon, William told Paul to move the Timer and place it between the two. It took only a moment for Paul to move the Timer between his two friends, dropping it to the ground.

Looking up at Paul, William held up a thumb and said, "Okay, let's get inside and start the countdown to home."

"Ice cream, here I come!" Bob said as he and Ellie walked to the Timer and climbed the ladder. William started up after them. Relief was in the air as they prepared for the flight home.

William was nearly at the top when a loud ping sounded off the side of the craft, only a few feet away. It was a shot. In just seconds, several more ricocheted off the ship's sloping side. Looking around, the friends saw the other timer topping a rise one hundred and fifty yards away. It was to their front and north of them, the men on its bridge firing away. They could see Bob's great adversary, standing taller than any of the others, pointing and directing the shooters.

"How did they get here ahead of us?" yelled Bob, reaching to give his brother a hand.

Suddenly, William turned and leaped to the ground. "We've got to get those beacons!" Running to the closest one, he snatched it up and ran for the second. As dirt from bullets erupted all around him, he grabbed the second beacon, spun, and ran for the ladder. He rapidly climbed it, holding the beacons in his left hand. Then he pulled himself over the top railing with his right.

William took two steps toward the hatch when a bullet knocked the two metal rods out of his hand. They landed on the deck and rolled toward the side. William dove for them and grabbed one but watched helplessly as the second beacon slid over the edge and falling to the ground.

William sprang up, throwing one leg over the railing, prepared to leap to the ladder below. Suddenly, a hand reached out and grabbed a handful of the back of William's jumpsuit. "No time, William, it's going to be close as it is. We need to get below fast," Paul said, releasing William and standing back.

Turning to Paul and looking indecisive, William pulled away, not sure what to do. He took two quick steps to the open hatch, descending the ladder with Paul right on his heels. Paul pulled the hatch cover down behind him and locked it into place.

Paul stood still for a moment, resting his forehead on a rung while holding the ladder with both hands. Slowly turning to face William, he said, "William, I'm sorry. I just knew if you went after that last beacon, you would never make it back up the ladder without getting shot. I couldn't stand by and let that happen."

"You, were right. You probably saved my life," William said, making a fist and tapping his friend's shoulder.

"Will you two quit talking and strap yourselves in!" Bob shouted. He hastily flipped switches.

Paul and William rushed to their seats as Bob reached for a lever in the center of the console and pulled it down. After a pause, there was the vibration, then darkness, and the jolting move to the left.

"Boy, I hope we can get out of here before the other timer smashes into us," Bob said, leaning back in his chair. There was nothing to do but sit and worry.

In a few seconds, there were several pops, jolts, jerks, the rising in the air sensation, and the cotton candy on the window. Then they were gone. Barely, just barely, they had made it!

CHAPTER 32

HOME

Bob still held the lever when there was one last jolt; the Timer dropped from a foot in the air onto the concrete floor in the white room in northwest Wyoming. They were back in the twenty-first century. The crew looked at each other, sighed, and then smiles began breaking out, one after the other.

"I can't believe we made it," Ellie said, unfastening her seat belt. "I was so scared one of you would be shot. I've had enough of nursing my friends and their gunshot wounds."

"Well, let's see what's going on outside," Paul said as he unlocked the hatch, pushing it so that it fell open with a metallic clang. They could hear an alarm; it sounded like a submarine gong preparing to crash-dive. He took a few tentative steps up the ladder, raising his head through the hatch and peeking out. The first thing he saw was Dailey pushing through a door onto a small landing above some steps. As soon as Dailey saw Paul, he smiled, laughed, and danced a short jig, obviously very happy to see them.

Paul climbed the rest of the ladder and stepped out onto the top deck. The others quickly joined him, lining up and looking down at Dailey.

"I'm so glad to see you, guys! I had confidence in you, but I have to admit I still worried a little."

"Well, Dailey, to be honest, there were times when we worried too," Bob said, with a big smile.

Then Spear stepped from behind Bob with a bit of hesitancy. This had to be the strangest place he had ever seen.

"Hey, you brought back a new friend! Well, bring him down to meet me. I won't bite."

The look on Spear's face said he wasn't so sure of that. Taking in the alien room, not to mention the talk of biting, was very different from anything he knew. That feeling would only increase over the next few minutes.

"Dailey, we had a great time, but we are glad to be back. Wait until you hear about some of the things we saw and did," William said, climbing down from the Timer and walking over to give Dailey a big hug.

William's hug was followed by Paul's and Ellie's. Bob walked over, picked Dailey up, and swung him around.

"You know, this has kind of been a tradition for Bob to pick me up like that since he was in seventh grade. He was big enough and strong enough even then."

Putting an arm around Ellie's shoulders, Dailey asked, "Who do you have here with you?"

Smiling, Bob said, "Dailey, this is Spear. He is here from 1805."

Dailey walked over, looked at Spear, and said, "You have got to be kidding!" He reached out and took Spear's hand. "Sure glad to have you here with us."

Spear looked relieved. There had been no biting.

Ellie put her hand to her mouth. "Look at the Timer!"

"What about it?" asked Bob.

"It's clean!" Ellie said, walking to their ship and running her small hand over the surface. There was not a speck of dirt, dust, or mud anywhere on its gleaming surface.

"It was always that way when we got back," observed Dailey. "We didn't know why, but we were always happy about it."

The others walked to the Timer, amazed at its transformation. Paul even climbed the ladder and inspected the upper deck but could not find anything marring the shiny surface.

"Anyone hungry?" asked Dailey. "We were always starving when we got back. Come on in the kitchen, and I'll see if I can rustle up something."

"Yea!" Bob shouted, leaping up the steps and onto the landing.

"Just like his daddy. His first stop was always the refrigerator. If we didn't have something he wanted, we headed into Jackson to get it."

Bob led the way into the shiny kitchen. He opened the refrigerator, and satisfied there was plenty to eat, he walked back to the others and joined them at the table.

Dailey placed two pitchers of milk on the table, along with three large cartons of ice cream. "For some reason, when Mr. Wattson and I got back, we always wanted milk and ice cream. It became a ritual for us. I hope you'll enjoy this."

"I think you can count on it, Dailey," Bob said after a big swallow of milk that gave him a white mustache.

Ellie leaned over and filled a bowl full of vanilla and fudge ice cream. She slid the bowl over to Spear and handed him a spoon, a utensil with which he had become very proficient. While the others watched expectantly, he helped himself to the ice cream and, as usual, placed it on his tongue. His solemn expression changed into a wide smile, and the others cheered. Picking up a jar of multicolored sprinkles, Ellie shook some into his bowl. Taking another sample, Spear's smile was bigger.

Dailey broke into a smile as wide as Spear's, happy watching people enjoy food, especially his cooking. "I believe he likes homemade ice cream," he said, nodding toward Spear. "What about rib eye steaks, baked potatoes, and cowboy beans for supper tonight?"

This was greeted with enthusiastic approval, especially from Bob who threw his cap in the air.

"I don't know about the rest of you, but I've got to take a shower before I do anything else. I feel like I need to vacuum myself before I shower, or all this dust will turn to mud," William said, running his hands down his sides and looking utterly disgusted.

The others, especially Paul, also really wanted to get clean and into fresh clothes. As William and Paul walked down the hall, a light cloud of dust seemed to follow their every step. Dailey agreed with the showers since he didn't like anything messing up his clean home.

"Throw those dirty clothes into the hamper in your rooms. I'll pick them up in the morning and have them washed," Dailey ordered as they filed out of the room.

William selected a room for Spear and took him into the bathroom, reaching over and turning the shower on then off. This act amazed Spear. William showed him several times until Spear could do it himself.

The next step was introducing shampoo, which doubled as body wash. William knew Spear was familiar with it because he had used it several times but never in a shower. William would show him what to do. William unzipped his jumpsuit, slipped out his arms, and tied the sleeves around his waist. He removed his filthy T-shirt, dropping it into a dirty-clothes hamper. After wetting his hair under the shower, William squirted soap into his hands and rubbed it vigorously in his scalp for a minute. Then he put his sudsy head back under the shower. The water running out of his hair was dirty as it swirled down the drain. Twice more he repeated the procedure before daring to take a white, fluffy towel off a stack next to the shower.

Next, he pantomimed washing of the rest of his body. Placing a clean towel by the shower, he motioned Spear to remove his clothes and get in.

"I'll be back in a short time," William said, walking out of the bathroom. He returned a few minutes later with an armful of clothes. By now, Spear was out of the shower, drying himself and appearing clean. Tossing the clothes over the back of a chair and thinking there was nothing else he could do to assist, William walked out and hurried to his bathroom where he happily jumped into his own shower. Never had hot water and soap felt so good or been so needed. Afterward, William pulled on clean clothes, socks, and boots. Then he retrieved Spear, and they walked back to the kitchen. He felt like a new man.

By then, all the friends had returned in clean jumpsuits with clean faces, clean hair, and big smiles. It was amazing how invigorated they felt. Being clean was a treat they had almost forgotten.

Bob had even shaved for the first time in two weeks, claiming his face to be soft as a baby's.

Then they all noticed a problem; Spear's hair was tangled and in his eyes. William realized he hadn't given him a comb or brush. They walked back to his room where William found a brush. Handing it to Spear, the problem was quickly solved.

Dailey had set the table. Each plate held a large, grilled rib eye steak and a hot baked potato wrapped in foil. There were two large red-and-white striped bowls of cowboy beans, two plates with sticks of butter, and two smaller striped bowls of sour cream. A tray of crescent rolls, covered by a red-and-white plaid napkin, completed the menu. There also were pitchers of milk and iced tea. A feast!

Bob helped Spear with his potato as Ellie handed him his knife and fork. He had some experience with a knife and fork and started right in on the steak. Bob, after preparing the potato, sprinkled a little salt and pepper on the corner of Spear's steak and watched, in satisfaction, as his Indian smiled in enjoyment.

Taking another bite, Spear said, "Good, very good." His verbal skills were limited, but his usage continued to improve.

William laughed and slapped the table. "You know what, he speaks with a southern accent, just like Ellie!"

"I think he sounds like a gentleman," Ellie said, nodding of her head knowingly.

Soon, everyone but Ellie had finished their steak and potato. She told Dailey it was wonderful but more than she could eat. The boys had also made sure most of the beans were gone.

All said, it was the best meal they had ever eaten. Only Bob wanted dessert as the others were too full. He opted for a large piece of apple pie and a double scoop of vanilla ice cream.

Crooking his finger at Spear, William said, "Come on, we need to finish your wardrobe."

The others looked down and saw Spear wore no shoes or socks.

They followed the two boys into the fitting room and watched as William began fitting Spear his shoes. First, he gave him a pair of medium-weight white athletic socks and then began measuring his feet. After checking the width and length, he left the room and returned carrying some hiking boots exactly like his own. He held them out to Spear who seemed very pleased with his new present. William motioned for Spear to sit down then knelt and guided his feet into place. It took only a minute showing him how to lace his boots before Spear took over. As with all ropes and knots, he caught on immediately. His manual dexterity, especially with knots, was amazing. In a few seconds, he had both boots laced and secured with an intricate knot.

Spear stood up and swayed unsteadily. "They feel very disagreement to my feet."

"Gosh!" said Ellie. "Spear, perhaps it's difficult or different?"

"Different, yes, different. That's right. Different!"

The others realized he had never worn modern shoes or boots, only the soft, form-fitting moccasins. He tottered a little but steadied himself and walked across the room. They assured him he would soon get used to them.

William felt he had done a good job fitting him but knew there was the possibility of a blister or two. Placing his hand on one of Spear's new boots, William told him to be sure and let him know if they began to hurt his feet.

Bob looked at his brother. "William, you think it's time to show the crew the rest of the house?"

"I do." Turning to his friends, he said, "You going to be a part of something else you didn't know about, but it will affect you. It will kind of close the circle on why we selected you and what you stand to gain by joining us. Your perceptions of us, and your lives, are about to change."

"William, you're scaring me. Is it something bad?" asked Ellie, looking concerned.

"No, I don't think so nor do I believe you will think it bad. It's just different. Bob and I wanted to make sure we were making a good decision about you two. You came through with flying colors."

Bob held out his hand to Ellie. "Come on, it is really bad and really scary."

Ellie made a fist and hit Bob's shoulder. This caused no notice-able discomfort to Bob but caused her to laugh and rub her knuckles. She swung her arm through his, and they walked across the room.

At the end of the corridor, there was a metal door with the now-familiar control box with letters and numbers. William punched in a combination, and the door slid open to reveal yet another wide corridor like those that extended into the mountain. There were doors evenly spaced down both walls.

William walked to the first door on the left and turned the doorknob. He reached inside, turned on overhead lights, and walked down three steps to the floor.

"This is the Gem Room."

The others followed. Ellie and Paul gasped. The room was twenty-by-twenty feet, and the floor was practically covered by gems of every hue. There were thousands of uncut stones scattered about. Gallon plastic buckets filled with gems of the same color had been spilled over on to the floor in untidy piles three and four inches high. There were old wooden boxes two-by-two feet filled with gems of the same color or mixed. It was an amazing variety.

"What are all the different colors?" asked Paul.

"William, you are better at naming the different colors than I," Bob said as he differed to his brother.

"Well, let's see," said William as he began to walk among the buckets. "The red are rubies and garnets, the pink tourmalines, the blue sapphires, lapis lazuli, and topaz. The green are emeralds and peridot, the yellow citrine and fire opals, the cool purple ones are amethyst, the bronze are tiger's eye, the black and clear are diamonds and some multicolored opals. I think there is even a box of pearls somewhere around here."

"We played in here when we were little. Dad and Dailey had everything neat and orderly until William and I came along. We are kind of responsible for all the mixing of stones," said Bob with a laugh. "This one was our Christmas box." He pointed to a Christmas cookie tin filled with rubies and emeralds.

Ellie sat down on a box that still had a lid nailed in place. "It looks like a room full of marbles. I bet there isn't another room in the world like this one," she said as she held a handful of sapphires before tossing them back in a bucket. Spear picked up an emerald and stared through it at one of the overhead lights.

Paul bent over, scooped up a double handful of stones from one of the mixed boxes, and let them trickle through his fingers. "How did you end up with all these?" he asked in wonderment.

William walked over and sat down next to Ellie. "Dad was a good trader and got some that way. Mostly, he knew where to look. He researched mining records and had a good knowledge of geology. He and Dailey went on lots of trips, staying for weeks at a time. They would choose an area and stay there until they got tired of looking. Almost everything was surface deposits with very little digging involved. They found the emeralds in Columbia, the rubies in the Mogok Valley of Burma, and the sapphires in Madagascar. The diamonds from volcanic pipes in South Africa did take some digging. He found some on the beaches, and some of the topaz came from Utah. There is a topaz from Brazil you might find interesting. Look in that box in the corner." He pointed to a dark wood box with brass hinges.

Ellie and Paul walked over to the box, and Paul lifted the lid. "Wow!" Ellie exclaimed.

Paul picked up an uncut yellow topaz the size of a basketball. "I don't believe it!" he said. "How big is it?"

Bob stood with his back against the wall, one foot propped back against it. "No idea how many carats, but it weighs about thirty-five pounds. Much bigger have been found, but that's the biggest Dad and Dailey ever found."

Ellie turned to William. "Did your father ever have any of these gems cut?"

"Not too many. Even the gems in the stairs are rough. He thought them much prettier cut, but never had much interest in it. Mom was dead, he didn't need the money, and he sure wasn't going to have any made into jewelry for me and Bob. I think he didn't care at all about the monetary value. He just liked hunting for them."

Paul walked over to his buddy Bob and put his hand on his shoulder. "Bob said treasure rooms, are there others? Can you top this one?"

"Depends on what you like. C'mon."

Bob led them out of the room, pushed open the first door on the right, and said, "Welcome to the Gold Room."

When he flipped on the light, the friends encountered a dazzling, golden sight. Wooden boxes lining the walls were piled high with gold nuggets. In some boxes were heavy, clear, plastic bags filled with gold dust. Piled in one corner were chunks of quartz, thick bands of gold running through them.

Ellie looked at William. "Where did your dad find all this gold?"

"Lots of different places. He found part of it in Canada, California, and Colorado. Ever heard of Sutter's Mill? He got part of it from South America. I think other than the US, most of it was found in Russia and South Africa."

Bob spoke up, "Dad said some of this was work. They could pinpoint future mine sites easily. They would blast into one and work through the broken quartz. They brought back lots of small quartz pieces and worked out the gold later. The pieces had to fit into the Timer. There are gold and quartz rocks used as paperweights and doorstops in all of his houses."

"Dad said the easiest gold they ever found was in the Yukon. There was a curve in a river there with a wide, flat sandbar. He said he and Dailey panned gold nuggets and put them in piles on the bank until they gave out. They were getting so many nuggets they didn't bother with flakes."

Bob laughed and said, "Yeah, and we still own the mineral rights to a mountain claim at the head of that river."

"How much gold is in this room?" asked Paul.

"I asked Dad one time," said Bob. "Dad said, just guessing, maybe a ton or two. That's not counting the weight of the quartz."

"Two to four thousand pounds!" exclaimed Paul.

"That is a lot of gold!" added Ellie.

Paul quickly added, "That's a lot of money!"

With not a hint of pretension, William replied, "It just depends on the day. You know, the value of gold changes every day."

Ellie reached into a box and pulled out an odd, twisted piece of gold. "What is this?'

"That's rope gold. See how it looks like a twisted rope. Dad would have found that in Russia," said William.

Bob smiled again and said, "Our estimated weight doesn't count what's in those old wooden chests in the corner. Go open one."

Two wooden chests banded with metal straps sat in a corner. They were two feet deep, four feet long, and three feet wide. Paul opened one. His eyes widened as he saw that it was filled to the top with shiny gold coins of all sizes. He opened the other one, and it was the same.

"He found hundreds of gold coins. Dad knew almost exactly when and where shipwrecks occurred. The Caribbean, and especially the Gulf of Mexico, are relatively shallow. Dad and Dailey were excellent divers. They carried inflatable rafts and diving gear and could get to some of the wrecks quite easily. Time was also a big factor in helping them. They could get to a wreck site before sand covered the ship or it was torn apart. They could park the Timer at or near a wreck site for days at a time. It could hover over the water. Back then, there was no dispute over treasure between nations or insurance companies. There were no territorial waters because there were no nations. Basically, everything on this side of the Atlantic was international waters, and treasure wrecks were open game."

"Bob's right. That has certainly changed now but not four or five hundred years ago. If Spain, for instance, knew where a wreck occurred, they would do a pretty good job of salvaging it themselves."

"William, remember when Dad told us about almost getting caught out in the gulf by a hurricane?"

"I do."

"Dad said there was no warning, the horizon started getting black, and by the time Dailey came up from a dive, the water was white capping. They pulled everything aboard as fast as they could and headed for land. By the time they made the beach, the waves were almost breaking over the Timer."

"What did they do?" asked Paul.

"They drove inland and finally landed in an open field away from trees on the leeward side of a small hill."

With a puzzled expression, Paul asked, "What is the leeward side?"

"The leeward side is opposite from the direction of the wind. The windward side is the direction the wind is coming from. The hill broke the wind just enough to give them shelter from the worst of the storm. Dad said it was still exciting."

"Not too much weather service back then," added Ellie.

William turned to Ellie and Paul, "Have you seen enough in here for now?"

"I think so," Paul said, hefting a marble-sized nugget. "Unreal how heavy this stuff is."

Spear placed several gold coins in his palm and moved it up and down before speaking, "Heavy, unreal stuff."

"There isn't too much to see in the next room, but it's kind of interesting. It's the Document Room," said William, walking out the door. Ellie, Spear, then Paul and Bob followed.

William went to the second room on the left and opened the Document Room door. Greenish-gray filing cabinets lined the walls; there was a heavy, wooden table in the center with black leather desk chairs on each side and each end.

Paul walked to the filing cabinets, smiling, and asked, "What do they have in them? Documents?"

William laughed and said, "They contain titles, deeds, and legal documents."

"Can we look?" asked Ellie.

"Sure," Bob replied.

Ellie slid open a drawer and took out the first file. It contained a parchment-like document stamped with a gold seal. "It's a deed from Silver City, New Mexico."

William leaned over her shoulder and looked at it. "It's from there, but the property is really outside Silver City. A long time ago, Dad bought a big ranch near there for fifty cents an acre. Bob and I spent many summers there with Dailey working cows."

"Were you real cowboys?" Ellie asked with a giggle.

"Not at first but as real as could be before it was over. We could round up cows with the best of them."

"Who looked after the ranch over the years, and how did the taxes get paid?" asked Paul.

"Dad took a page out of the King Ranch's book. In the 1850s, Captain King moved a destitute Mexican village to the ranch. These cowboys became known as Kineno's or 'King's men.' Dad brought five impoverished Mexican vaqueros and their families there. He set them up in houses and arranged for them to get paid. With only minimal direction from Dailey, they have run the ranch ever since. All five of the original families are still represented on the ranch, and they divide all the profit. Dad, and later Dailey, made certain any of the children that wanted an advanced education received one. About ten years ago, one of the great-granddaughters graduated from our school."

Ellie clapped her hands. "What an amazing, wonderful story!"

Paul then asked, "How big is the ranch?"

Bob laughed. "Very, very big."

"Let me ask again, if your dad or Dailey wasn't around, how did he keep the taxes paid and handle any legal problems?"

"Dad had a law degree and was a wiz with financial things. He set up an escrow account with a local bank. Their trust department paid the taxes and any other necessary expenses. If he had a legal problem, they would either handle it in house or farm it out to a law firm. Plus, either Dad or Dailey would go back every few years to check on things. Sometimes, they would go back and stay a while."

Ellie looked over another document and said, "What assets would he take to pay bills or the taxes? He couldn't bring cash, write a check, or put it on a credit card."

"Don't forget the Gold Room. Dad would sometimes have to take additional funds back to the bank, law firm, or an agent of some kind. He would take small gold bars in a sturdy briefcase. It worked every time. There would probably be a lot more gold here except for those trips."

"Wasn't he afraid of being robbed?"

"I don't think so. He always took Dailey, and they were armed. Plus, when you see a picture of Dad, you'll understand why he wasn't afraid."

Ellie shuffled through more files and discovered deeds from all over the United States and numerous foreign countries. "You, guys, are really, really rich!"

"Have we ever acted rich?' asked William.

"Never."

"Right, and we'll continue to act the same, and you'll continue to treat us the same. We've never cared whether you had money or not. You are just our friends. I suspect you've never cared whether we had money either."

"Nope, you're just William and Bob," she replied, turning to look at them.

"Dad bought ranches all over the West though usually in Wyoming, Montana, or Colorado. He really liked the country in those states, and he liked the mountains," said Bob.

William looked up from a file. "We own property in Hawaii too. Some of the vacant lots and fields you see around big cities are ours. Dad was pretty good at purchasing properties in the direction cities would grow. He would pay above market for empty land and sit on it. We have some urban buildings, but he never developed very much. I guess he just never got around to it. Bob and I have talked about starting a foundation strictly to build parks and recreational areas on some of this land."

"Dad also liked to build hideaways in the mountains and on islands. William and I are not sure where they all are. Not even Dailey knows where they all are."

Folding both arms across her chest, Ellie asked, "How do you keep up with all this property? Surely there is upkeep, taxes, I guess some salaries?"

"Well, Dailey helps. Plus, through Dad's estate, we have law firms and accountants we pay lots of money each year," answered William.

"Actually, William, that is lots and lots of money," said his brother. "Yeah, Paul, if you ever need tickets to see the Yankees or

Mets, we can help. I think the firms that handle Dad's estate would be more than happy to supply us some," Bob said smiling.

"How many of these hideaways do you two know about?" asked Ellie.

"Bob and I have been to about a dozen, but I'm sure there are others we don't know about. Dad said he had a list, but after looking through his safe and some of these files, we haven't found it yet. We've talked with Dailey, but he didn't know where the list was either. He said Dad didn't tell him everything."

Paul stood there with his mouth open. "What will happen to them?"

"If we don't find the list, I guess they will eventually fall down. He was very good about making sure they were tightly sealed up, but eventually, the weather or vandals will get to them. Most of the ones that we know about in the mountains are sturdy cabins. Typically, they are log cabins with porches, stone fireplaces, and hitching rails in front. They are nothing really fancy," said William, shrugging his shoulders.

"Hitching rail?" queried Paul.

"The only ways to get to most of them are either hiking or horseback. Dad chose the locations for their views, not their convenience. Several are pretty elaborate, but they're closer to roads and civilization."

"There is one Dad kept up, and we watch over now. He owned some land in the Bighorns in Wyoming. When he married our mother, he had a house built there and gave it to her as a wedding present. It has the mountain views, a big waterfall, meadows with elk. It pretty much has it all. It was bigger than the rest of his hideaways, with two stories, lots of bedrooms, huge stone fireplaces, and lots of artwork he let our mother choose from his collection. He planned it for a large family. Dailey said after our mom died, Dad told him to keep it up, but he never visited again."

"Oh," said Ellie, pensively, putting her left hand to her mouth.

"Well, William and I have happened on a couple of others when we were hiking on some of our property. One of them was in the Colorado Mountains and the other in the Prospect Mountains in Wyoming."

"How did you know they were yours?" asked Ellie.

"They were on our property."

Bob shrugged and turned his palms up. "Come on, let's go to the next room. It's our favorite."

Bob crossed the hall and pushed open another door, "Welcome to the Artist Room."

He turned on the lights, and Paul and Ellie stood there astonished. This room was about twice as big as the others. Framed pictures were stacked everywhere, along with built-in shelves filled with rolls of canvas. Canvases lay flat, stacked three-and four feet high. Painting after painting lined the walls. William named artists and pointed to their paintings. There were works by Miró, Chagall, Picasso, Titian, Vermeer, Raphael, and many others. He pointed out a statue by Donatello. There were hundreds of paintings and dozens of pieces of statuary. It was a veritable museum.

Ellie stood with hands on hips. "We studied about all these guys in art appreciation last year in school. I've never heard of this many together that were not in a public or private museum."

"And you probably never will," William said, laughing. "Of the many things Dad enjoyed doing and there were many, this may have been his favorite."

"When Dad bought many of these paintings, they were inexpensive. He said the adage about the starving artist was correct. Most have never even been listed in the artists' inventory, having been painted before the artists became famous. Dad said he would go to some of the artists before they attained fame and buy everything they had finished. He would pay what they asked and still get great bargains. He said this kept some of them alive. They were excited when he showed up."

"I'll bet," allowed Paul.

"Some of these were expensive when he bought them but not compared to what they're worth now. Inventory from the Gold Room helped purchase of all these," said Bob.

"What are they worth?" asked Paul.

"No telling," replied William. "Dad liked art and thought it a good investment. He asked what else could he buy a hundred or two hundred years ago that would be worth so much more now."

"You know what? He was right," said Ellie.

"Actually, it's funny. Dad's favorite artist was Charles Russell. He loved western art. He scattered Mr. Russell's work around his properties. Dad knew and liked him and said his work was better than the highbrow stuff. Regardless, the highbrow stuff was a good investment too," said Bob.

William held up a signed Russell showing the famous buffalo skull by the signature. "Several paintings this size have sold for $5 million. Not highbrow but pretty good."

"William and I have wondered about something. We think Dad may have told Mr. Russell about being able to travel through time. He hinted at it, but we could never pin him down. We've wondered if Mr. Russell thought him crazy, but as far as we know, they stayed friends. In fact, at the Charles Russell Museum in Great Falls, they have his studio set up on the grounds. There are brushes in there that Dad said he bought in Denver not too many years ago and took back to Mr. Russell in Great Falls. He pointed them out to us when we visited one year. There are personal notes in the Document Room he gave Dad over the years. He sketched in the margins and always started with 'Friend Bill.'"

"William and I hate we can't expand the historical inventory of lots of these artists, but how would we explain them? It would direct so much unwanted attention on us, so we just can't do it. The authentication process would eat us up. We've never sold or shown one, and I guess we never will."

"Dad started framing some of them to hang in this facility and some of his homes. He died before finishing," said William with a sigh.

"How did he die?" asked Paul.

"He was badly wounded on a trip to ancient Greece. Dailey got him back, but he died before they could get to a hospital."

"It's about the only thing Dailey doesn't like to talk about," added Bob.

"Dad did leave us a short letter. He told us to guard the secret of the Timer because there are too many people that might make bad use of it. He also mentioned something about certain persons trying to take it. Dailey said he was going in and out of consciousness at the end, and the words kind of drifted off into a scribble. Bob and I couldn't read the rest."

The friends walked around for a few minutes, unrolling canvas after canvas and looking through stacks of framed pictures. There were unknown artists as well as the famous. William said his father bought what he liked.

"Some of those unknown artists are now quite well-known. Dad had a good eye," said William.

"This has been amazing! I can't get over all the things your father was able to collect," said Paul.

William laughed as he was rolling a canvas back up. "Dad had lots more than this. We have one more room that has nothing but ancient weapons. It's not that interesting, but we'll make a quick walk-through. We have a warehouse filled with all kinds of things he brought back."

"Like what?" Asked Ellie.

"Shields, armor, weapons, cloth, clothes, more rugs, small furniture, vases, goblets, tableware. You name it," Bob said, shaking his head slowly.

"We have a Greek spear, shield, and helmet from the Battle of Thermopylae," said Bob. "Or a musket from Pickett's Charge at Gettysburg."

"You have those?" asked Ellie.

"Those and a ton more. The warehouse looks like a storage facility for a movie company. He had more weaponry and breastplates than a museum. There is a Gutenberg Bible and an original script from one of Shakespeare's plays. He brought back lots of historical things. He would label and put them away. He grouped things by country and era so it's easy to track something down. Sometimes, he used these items when traveling in the time period from which they came from. He said it helped him and Dailey blend in."

"Okay, this is a huge stretch, but Bob and I have wondered about how myths get started. Dad made many trips to ancient Greece. In reading his journals, he had some incredible adventures and pulled off some fairly heroic feats. He was a bigger and stronger man than anyone there had ever seen. We have wondered if he was the inspiration for the original Hercules."

"William, do you really think so?" Ellie exclaimed loudly.

William shrugged his shoulders. "Who knows? It's fun to think about."

Shaking his head, Paul looked at the brothers. "Wow! Okay, why show us all this now?"

Placing a hand on his friend's shoulder and glancing at Ellie, William began, "Bob and I wanted to make sure you were with us, rich or poor. We never thought you would want to join us for the money, but we had to find out. All the things we just showed you would turn almost anyone's head, but now we're not concerned."

"William's right. We've got plans to maybe do some worthwhile things with the Timer. We want you two to go along with us. If you ever thought you would have to worry about money, you can forget that now. We wanted you to see the rooms to know we're for real. We are still William and Bob, and the fact that we have lots of money shouldn't change how you feel about us. After all, you're rich as well. William and I intend to make part of all this yours as well."

"Bob, you know it wouldn't change how we feel about you two," said Ellie as she ran an index finger beneath her eyes.

"I know." Bob stood and held his hand high in the air, "We are all in this together!"

As with acceptance and acclamation, William, Paul, and Ellie joined their right hands with his.

Then William turned and motioned to Spear across the room. "Wait a minute. Spear come over here. Like it or not, you're also part of this crew."

With that, the five friends clasped hands in a standing salute as Bob yelled, "All for one and one for all!"

"This was all pretty amazing. Who would have ever figured you two would have all this? Unlike some of the others at school, you've have never mentioned having any money, much less this much!" Ellie said as they walked out of the room.

The friends had all enjoyed taking Spear on a tour of the various rooms and the interesting things they held. Of course, almost everything was new and interesting to him. He thought the jewels and gold were nice, but he loved the ancient weapons in the last room. He hefted the swords and pretended to throw a spear, which completely disconcerted William. Fortunately, he held on to the spear, moving next to an English morning star. Spear twirled the spiked ball around his head and through several intricate turns before placing it back on the floor. William sighed with relief when Spear next slid his arm into a Spartan shield that Mr. Wattson brought home from Thermopylae. William walked over and showed Spear the proper way to hold the heavy bronze shield with the inverted (V).

Moving along, they were surprised how much Spear loved the artwork. He was particularly taken by the horses and Indians in the oil Charles Russell paintings. He traced the lines with his fingers and was fascinated where the oil paint had been applied in its thickest layers. William made a mental note to take Spear to the Charles M. Russell Museum in Great Falls, Montana. He would have to remember to tell him to look but not touch.

Spear particularly enjoyed the television screens showing outside scenery, and he jumped back, startled, the first time some birds flew directly at the camera.

To everyone's amazement, it was early afternoon. They had totally lost track of time while getting home. They all decided to nap to help get them through the rest of the day. William took Spear to his room and turned down the bed. Ellie told him to get small sleep, making several hand signs.

As William and Ellie were about to leave, Spear told them, "Back in short time." He strode out the door and turned down the hall. William and Ellie exchanged puzzled looks, sitting down to wait for his return. In five minutes, Spear walked back in the door with his beloved sleeping bag under his arm. Pulling on the Velcro straps, he tossed it on the bed. Contentedly, he crawled inside as his friends quietly left the room.

CHAPTER 33

THE PAST IN THE FUTURE?

UNTIL THEY LAY down, the friends had no idea how tired they were. They had traveled hard and slept fitfully for days. The beds and clean sheets were another thing they had taken for granted before their trip. It was late afternoon before they gathered in the viewing room. As they trickled in, they found Spear already there, moving from screen to screen in total fascination. He gingerly touched a finger to some of the images moving across the monitor.

After watching Spear, the others gathered in one of the sofa and chair groupings. William wanted to discuss the trip and the future. It was a given they would return to school. William, Ellie, and, to some extent, Paul were certainly more enthusiastic than Bob, but he agreed that it was necessary.

"How are you, guys, fixed for money?" William asked Ellie and Paul.

"I have enough," Paul said.

"I'm fine," was Ellie's response.

"Liars," said William, chuckling. "I gave Dailey your information before we left. Any school bills will be paid. Dailey has arranged for money to be deposited in your school accounts each month. This is the least we can do after we misled you about the summer job."

"Thanks," Ellie said, getting up and to give Bob and William each a big hug. Her eyes seemed a little moist as she sat back down.

"I feel like we should be paying you, guys, for the summer we just had. That was really special!" Paul said, leaning forward and looking both Bob and William in the eye.

Rubbing a fingertip beneath each eye, Ellie looked at her friends. "It will be a little different not worrying about money every month."

Looking across the room at their friend, William said, "What do we do about Spear? We brought him here, and his welfare is our responsibility. I don't know if school is an option right now."

"I think I have a solution, William," said Dailey. They had not seen him walk to the room. He had stood quietly, listening to their conversation.

"Believe it or not, Paul and Ellie, I have a college education thanks to William and Bob's father. I would love to homeschool Spear until we can make other arrangements," Dailey said as he sat in a vacant chair.

I really don't know any subject in which Dailey is not well-versed. He helped me with my homework many a night," Bob said earnestly.

"I would like teaching. Also, I would enjoy having company around for a change. I bet in a few months, you won't believe how well our friend, Spear, will be able to speak and function. His helping me around here will be great. I can tell he has a bright, quick mind."

They all agreed that this would be the perfect solution. It would certainly work at least until Spear got better acquainted with the modern world.

Dailey and Ellie pulled Spear aside and, through words and hand signs, explained what they had in mind. Spear responded with a vigorous nodding of his head and a wide smile. After his initial fear of being bitten, he realized Dailey was a warm, caring person. They joined the others in the kitchen. Bob was looking through the refrigerator again, saying he was starved.

Dailey made sandwiches and milkshakes for supper. Everyone had a choice of chocolate or vanilla, with chocolate the overwhelming favorite. He also baked a chocolate layer cake and served it with vanilla ice cream. Spear said it was the best thing he had ever eaten. Everyone agreed.

Teasing Spear, Paul said that eating Dailey's food every day would make him as big as a horse.

Spear linked his fingers, held his arms in a circle out in front of him, and said, "Or Bob."

Everyone laughed raucously, especially Bob.

When the laughter subsided, Dailey beckoned Spear with a crooked finger. "Come on, Spear, I want to show you what a snowmobile looks like. We'll have a big time on them in a few months.

The others walked to the viewing room and took seats. Bob and Paul lay on sofas while William and Ellie chose chairs and propped their feet on a coffee table. Everyone was beat.

William decided to explain why he tried so hard to get the homing devices. "The reason I wanted to get them was because of something Dailey told me. He said to be careful not to lose them because others might be able to track us with them. Until the other timer showed up, I had no idea what he was talking about. He said that they could possibly track us because of an electronic code on them. This code is supposed to leave a trail in the past as well as the present. Don't ask me how. I didn't know then, and I don't understand it now."

"Leave a trail through time?" Bob asked.

"Yes, but we really don't know if the others know anything about us. Although you do have to wonder how they showed up in the same place and same time as us."

"I think we better presume the beacons do leave some sort of trail or signal. It's too much of a coincidence," Bob said.

"Yeah, but maybe they didn't find it. Maybe they didn't even know I dropped it."

"I repeat, I think we better presume they did."

Swinging her feet to the floor and standing up, Ellie put her hands on her hips and said, "I don't understand. I suspect there is nothing Dailey can tell me that will help. I believe what he said is true, and I think if we go again, we'd better be on guard."

They pondered being tracked by the other timer if they returned to the past. There was probably a way to change the code, but no one knew how to do it.

"Dailey said he doesn't think they can track us to an exact location, but they can get to the general area. Also, he does think they can get the time exact," William said, tucking another sofa cushion behind his head.

"Well, that big guy better watch out because I'm going again," Bob said, looking combative.

Looking at his friend, Paul said, "Bob, if he could see that look on your face right now, I don't think he would want any part of you."

William laughed softly. "Okay, where to next?"

"One of the nice things about time travel is that you can go to the same place, just at another time, and it's different," Paul said.

Bob placed his chin in his right palm. "I've thought about the Indian cultures in the southeast or the Iroquois in the northeast near our school. How about another national park like Yosemite, Glacier, or Mesa Verde? How about seeing the California or Yukon gold rush?"

"How about the Aztec in the Yucatan or the Inca in Peru?" chimed in Ellie.

"I would want to go but before all the diseases almost wiped them out," agreed Bob.

"We'd better make sure we have our vaccinations!" added Paul. "We don't want to catch anything, but we sure don't want to bring any disease back with us or give it to others."

William smiled at all the suggestions. "You know, of course, I think we can travel worldwide. How about China during the time of the Khans or ancient Rome or Greece? There is Egypt or England during the time of the knights."

"Okay, I want to play," said Paul. "How about going to Easter Island or our Civil War or eastern Europe and Russia during the time of the Czars?"

William looked around at the eager faces. "The facts are we can go almost anywhere at any time, and that makes for tough decisions. We'll probably end up going somewhere we haven't even thought about."

"Makes you wonder how far back we can go," added his brother.

"We sure don't know."

"I have a question," said Ellie. "Do we have to stay two or three months each time? How about we go for a couple of weeks during the holidays?"

There was a chorus of "Christmas Holidays!"

"Holidays, Christmas?" replied Spear, looking curious.

"I can't wait for Christmas! Get ready somewhere in the past, here we come!" Bob said, jumping up and clapping his hands.

EPILOGUE

WILLIAM STEERED THE Jeep around hairpin curves and up the winding, mountain road leading to their school. Because of a light rain, he drove slowly, with Bob's constant encouragement to speed up. They, including Ellie and Paul, were on their way back to school. The trees lining the road were beginning to change their leaves to a riot of fall colors, red being the most prominent. The air was earthy, with a wet leaf smell, but was clean and invigorating.

Finally, the road flattened and threaded its way between two ten-foot square brick columns that formed the school's entrance. Granite obelisks topped the columns and had been painted by rival schools numerous times before big football games. Turning into a parking lot, William eased into a space behind their dorm, a long, two-story wooden building. They had enjoyed the ride from the airport, but it felt good to stretch their legs as they stepped out. Getting their bags, they walked around the corner, up the steps, and through the front door.

Down the hall to the left, they saw three husky boys they knew in a semicircle around a tall, gangling boy they didn't recognize. The three that had apparently cornered the fourth. They were three bullies who liked nothing better than intimidating new students, especially smaller, weaker ones.

"My three favorite guys," Bob said, dropping his bag and starting down the hall.

"Wait, wait a minute, Bob," said his brother, quickly following. "You, two, wait here," he said over his shoulder to Ellie and Paul.

Turning to Paul, Ellie said, "Donald Grant! He's always trying to pick on someone."

Quickly approaching the four boys, Bob said to the trapped stranger, "What's your name, pal?"

Looking fearful, the young boy touched his finger to his chest and said, "Me?"

"Yeah, right, you," Bob replied.

"My name is Jim," he replied, weakly and with a trembling voice.

With a laugh, Bob said, "Well, I thought that was my good friend, Jim." With that, he walked over and placed his large arm over the youngster's bony shoulders.

Turning to the center boy in the trio, a large fellow with bristled, white-blond hair, a tight T-shirt, and a round sneering face and a turned-up nose, Bob said, "What mischief are you up to now, Donny? Bothering my friend, Jim?"

Practically spitting out the words "You better run along while you still can, Wattson" was the rude, abrupt answer.

Dropping his arm from Jim's shoulders and taking a step forward, Bob put his hands on his hips and replied, "Donny, I'm not from running stock."

Donny Grant took a step back. "You think because you're bigger than me that I should be scared. There are three of us!"

Smiling, Bob retorted, "Bigger and tougher too. I'm telling you and your two sidekicks you better leave my friend, Jim, alone." With that, Bob threw his arm back over his new friend's shoulder. He walked deliberately forward and shoved Grant and the boy on the left to the side and made his way back down the hall. Neither Grant nor his friend said a word.

When Bob was a safe distance away, Donald Grant yelled after him, "That guy is just like you, your brother, and your two ratty friends down there. Poor, charity cases. You probably spent the summer working in a crummy hamburger joint trying to scrape up enough money for school. I don't know why they let your kind in here."

With a laugh and a wink at the others, Bob said, "Come on, guys, let's go upstairs and meet our good friend, Jim."

With their laughter rippling down the hall, they picked up their bags and climbed the stairs to their rooms.

ABOUT THE AUTHOR

B. G. HINES grew up in rural Alabama with a horse and bicycle in a town of 350. After high school, he attended and graduated from the University of Alabama. An indifferent student, the best thing he accomplished was getting another student, Sally Rogers, to marry him. They have a daughter and son, both with wonderful families, and five grandchildren. After a variety of jobs, including seven years at a bank, he got into the insurance business with Sally. His older brother has been a great influence on his life. He mailed B. G. a pair of running shoes, and he later ran two marathons. His brother wanted to climb the highest point in all fifty states, and B. G. became a cursory mountain climber. His best two peaks were Mt. Hood in Oregon and Gannett Peak in Wyoming. This led him to a love of the West. Yellowstone National Park is 1,900 miles from home, but he has been there thirty-two times. He loves Jackson Hole and has friends there. He served three times as a volunteer with the USFS in Northwest Wyoming.

His mother read to her children. This gave each child a love of books. At twelve, B. G. discovered the Hardy Boys. He liked their friends, their adventures, and their values. He thought one day he would like to emulate their values. He also found its great fun being able to make people do exactly what you want them to do and say what you want them to say. He likes to think William and Bob Wattson of his books set good examples for the youth of today.

Ingram Content Group UK Ltd.
Milton Keynes UK
UKHW010038070423
419774UK00001B/100